S0-BBI-414

IMPORTANT PRE-COLUMBIAN AND NATIVE AMERICAN ART

THE HENDERSHOTT COLLECTION – SESSION I

Heritage Signature Auction #643 • September 29, 2006 • New York City

LOT VIEWING IN DALLAS

Heritage Auction Galleries, 3500 Maple Avenue
10th Floor Gallery, Dallas, Texas 75219

Public Viewing
Tuesday, September 12, thru Friday, September 15
9:00 AM – 6:00 PM CT

Opening Reception
Tuesday, September 12, 5:00 – 8:00 PM CT

LOT VIEWING IN NEW YORK CITY

The Fletcher-Sinclair Mansion
(The Ukrainian Institute of America)
2 East 79th Street, New York 10021

Public Viewing
Tuesday, September 26, 2:00 – 8:00 PM ET
Wednesday, September 27 thru Thursday, September 28
9:00 AM – 6:00 PM ET or by appointment

FAX BIDDING

Deadline, Thursday, September 28, by 6:00 PM ET
Fax: 214-443-8425

INTERNET BIDDING

HA.com/FineArt • Bid@HA.com
Bidding closes Thursday, September 28, at 10:00 PM ET

LIVE TELEPHONE BIDDING

Customer Service: 866-835-3243
Must be arranged on or before Thursday, September 28,
by 5:00 PM ET

LIVE AUCTION SESSIONS IN NEW YORK CITY

The Fletcher-Sinclair Mansion
(The Ukrainian Institute of America)
2 East 79th Street, New York 10021

Session I
Pre-Columbian Art
Friday, September 29, at 10:00 AM ET
Lots 47001 – 47259

Session II
Native American Art
Friday, September 29, at 2:00 PM ET
Lots 48001 – 48234

Lots are sold at an approximate rate of 75 lots per hour.

View lots online at HA.com/FineArt

For Terms and Conditions of auction, see pp.238-239.

For explanation of Bidding Methods, see pp.240-241.

AUCTIONEERS

Kathleen Guzman   NY Day license #0762165
Samuel W. Foose   NY Day license #0952360
                  NY Night license #0952361

BUYER'S PREMIUM

19.5%

AUCTION RESULTS

Immediately available at HA.com/FineArt

LOT PICK-UP

By appointment. Call customer service at 866-835-3243

HERITAGE
Auction Galleries

Direct Customer Service Line: Toll-free 866-835-3243 (24-hour VM)
3500 Maple Avenue, 17th Floor, Dallas, Texas 75219-3941
214-528-3500 • 800-872-6467 • 214-443-8425 (fax)

THIS AUCTION IS CATALOGUED AND PRESENTED BY HERITAGE AUCTIONS, INC.

Catalogued by: John Lunsford

Edited by: John Lunsford, Mary Brinker, and Courtney E. Kennedy

Production and Design by: Mandy Bottoms, Cindy Brenner, Carlos Cardoza, Keith Craker, Lisa Fox,
Cathy Hadd, Mary Hermann, Matt Pegues, Michael Puttonen, Marsha Taylor, and Carl Watson

Catalogue and Internet Imaging by: Terry Thibeau, Ray Proska, Steve Robinson, John Noeding, Matt Roppolo, Kim Patterson, Haley Hagen,
Nina Castro, Tony Webb, Butch Ziaks, Bea Faustino, Shaun Zokaie, Chandler Thompson, Lucas Garritson, Colette Warren, and Lori McKay

Special thanks to Mary Brinker for her tireless assistance in the cataloguing and organization of this collection.
Also to Caitlin Owen, Emily Hoyle, and Erin Emerson for their invaluable assistance in producing this volume.

© 2006 Heritage Auctions, Inc.

HERITAGE
Auction Galleries

World Headquarters
3500 Maple Avenue, 17th Floor
Dallas, Texas 75219-3941
800-872-6467

HA.com/FineArt

Edmund P. Pillsbury, Ph.D.
Director of Fine & Decorative Arts
Ext. 533 • EPP@HA.com

Norma Gonzalez, Vice President Operations
Ext. 242 • Norma@HA.com

UNITED STATES COINS

HA.com/Coins
U.S. Coins

Leo Frese, Ext. 294
Leo@HA.com

Charles Clifford, Ext. 477
CharlesC@HA.com

Sam Foose, Ext. 227
SamF@HA.com

Jim Jelinski, Ext. 257
JimJ@HA.com

David Lewis, Ext. 520
DLewis@HA.com

David Lisot, Ext. 303
DavidL@HA.com

Bob Marino, Ext. 374
BobMarino@HA.com

David Mayfield, Ext. 277
DavidM@HA.com

Matt Orsini, Ext. 526
MattO@HA.com

Bob Phillips, Ext. 588
BobP@HA.com

Mike Sadler, Ext. 332
MikeS@HA.com

UNITED STATES COINS PRIVATE TREATY SALES

HA.com/Coins
Todd Imhof, Ext. 313
Todd@HA.com

CURRENCY

HA.com/Currency
Paper Money

Len Glazer, Ext. 390
Len@HA.com

Allen Mincho, Ext. 327
Allen@HA.com

Dustin Johnston, Ext. 302
Dustin@HA.com

Jim Fitzgerald, Ext. 348
JimF@HA.com

Michael Moczalla, Ext. 481
MichaelM@HA.com

WORLD COINS

HA.com/Coins
World Coins & Currencies

Warren Tucker, Ext. 287
WTucker@HA.com

Scott Cordry, Ext. 369
ScottC@HA.com

Harvey Gamer, Ext. 676
HarveyG@HA.com

COMICS

HA.com/Comics
*Comics, Original Comic Art
and Related Memorabilia*

Ed Jaster, Ext. 288
EdJ@HA.com

Lon Allen, Ext. 261
LonA@HA.com

MUSIC & ENTERTAINMENT MEMORABILIA

HA.com/Entertainment
*Stage-Worn Costumes, Records,
Signed Photos & Memorabilia*

Doug Norwine, Ext. 452
DougN@HA.com

John Hickey, Ext. 264
JohnH@HA.com

POLITICAL MEMORABILIA & AMERICANA

HA.com/Americana
*Historical & Pop Culture Americana,
Vintage Toys, Presidential & Political Memorabilia,
Buttons & Medals, Books & Manuscripts,
First Editions and Collectible Autographs*

Tom Slater, Ext. 441
TomS@HA.com

Marsha Dixey, Ext. 455
MarshaD@HA.com

John Hickey, Ext. 264
JohnH@HA.com

SPORTS COLLECTIBLES

HA.com/Sports
*Sports Cards, Artifacts,
Game-Used Jerseys & Equipment*

Chris Ivy, Ext. 319
CIvy@HA.com

Stephen Carlisle, Ext. 292
StephenC@HA.com

Jonathan Scheier, Ext. 314
JonathanS@HA.com

Mark Jordan, Ext. 187
MarkJ@HA.com

Mike Gutierrez, Ext. 183
MikeG@HA.com

VINTAGE MOVIE POSTERS

HA.com/MoviePosters
Posters, Lobby Cards, and Hollywood Ephemera

Grey Smith, Ext. 367
GreySm@HA.com

FINE ART

HA.com/FineArt
*Impressionist, Old Masters and
Contemporary Drawings, Paintings,
Sculpture and Photography*

Edmund P. Pillsbury, Ph.D., Ext. 533
EPP@HA.com

Ed Jaster, Ext. 288
EdJ@HA.com

Lucas Rigby, Ext. 483
LucasR@HA.com

Lindsay Davis, Ext. 542
LindsayD@HA.com

TEXAS ART

HA.com/TexasArt
Early Texas Art, Drawings and Paintings

Larry Boettigheimer, Ext. 523
LarryB@HA.com

ILLUSTRATION ART

HA.com/FineArt
Pinups and Illustration Art

Ed Jaster, Ext. 288
EdJ@HA.com

DECORATIVE ARTS

HA.com/FineArt
*Art Glass, European & American Silver,
Pottery & Ceramics*

Michael Wolf, Ext. 541
MWolf@HA.com

Tim Rigdon, Ext. 119
TimR@HA.com

Christine Carmody, Ext. 689
ChristineC@HA.com

JEWELRY & TIMEPIECES

HA.com/Jewelry
Jewelry & Timepieces

Jill Burgum, Ext. 697
JillB@HA.com

MEDIA RELATIONS

Marketing and Public Relations

Cathy Hadd, Ext 216
Cathy@HA.com

John Petty, Ext 283
JohnP@HA.com

CREDIT DEPARTMENT

Marti Korver, Ext 248
Marti@HA.com

CORPORATE OFFICERS

R. Steven Ivy, Co-Chairman
James L. Halperin, Co-Chairman
Gregory J. Rohan, President
Paul Minshull, Chief Operating Officer

Steve Ivy
CEO
Co-Chairman
of the Board

Jim Halperin
Co-Chairman
of the Board

Greg Rohan
President

Paul Minshull
Chief Operating
Officer

3500 Maple Avenue, 17th Floor, Dallas, Texas 75219-3941
214-528-3500 | 800-872-6467 | 214-443-8425 (fax)

FINE AND DECORATIVE ARTS

Edmund Pillsbury,
Ph.D.
Managing Director

John Lunsford
Senior Expert,
Pre-Columbian

Courtney E. Kennedy
Associate Managing
Director

Kathleen Guzman
Fine Art Representative/
Senior Expert

Michael Wolf
Deputy Managing
Director

Tom Slater
Director, Americana

FEW PEOPLE HAVE COLLECTED WITH THE PASSION AND INTELLECTUAL CURIOSITY of Gary Hendershott, whose important holdings of ancient and Native American art Heritage Auction Galleries is honored to have the opportunity to record for posterity in these fully-illustrated volumes of critical text.

Mr. Hendershott, like many others, fell in love with things of beauty as a boy, acquiring stamps, coins, arrowheads, and eventually all kinds of art and memorabilia. Through his acquisitions, he developed a lifelong fascination with history – an obsession for knowledge that has never abated. His interest in ritual and ceremony, rulers and warlords, the struggles and feats that have shaped society over time, has been insatiable. As a result, over more than three decades of ceaseless activity he has assembled collections of various kinds ranging from the beginnings of civilization in ancient Greece to the founding of American democracy in the eighteenth and nineteenth centuries.

None of these collecting pursuits has been more heartfelt and personal than his devotion to Pre-Columbian art in general and its later manifestation in Native American culture in particular. The Hendershott Collection possesses an outstanding array of gold artwork, primarily from Costa Rica, Panama, Columbia and Peru, dating from approximately 100 A.D. to 1500 A.D. Also noteworthy are his collections of Maya jades and great Peruvian weavings, which display a stunning range of color and textile techniques and date between 300 B.C. and 1500 A.D. Likewise, the Native American collection, filled with museum-quality objects, reflects the collector's personal tastes and interests. Featuring impressive examples of classic Navajo weavings and chiefs' blankets and a broad selection of Plains Indian works, the collection includes war shirts, war shields, tomahawks and Indian weaponry from the Comanche and Kiowa of the Southern Plains to the Cheyenne and Sioux of the Northern Plains. The highlight of the collection is a complete ledger book filled with thirty spectacular hand-colored drawings by the Sioux artist Walter Bone Shirt, one of the finest surviving examples of Indian painting of the nineteenth century and arguably the best of its kind still in private hands.

First and foremost, we have Gary Hendershott to thank for making his valuable and important collections available to Heritage Auction Galleries for publication and public sale. We must also express our sincere gratitude to those experts who have devoted countless hours to researching and cataloguing the works. In particular, we received invaluable assistance from John Lunsford, Curator Emeritus of the Dallas Museum of Art. Mr. Lunsford oversaw the development of the DMA's pre-eminent holdings of ancient American art over some twenty-eight years and also had a pivotal role in the enrichment of the Kimbell Art Museum's more select holdings in the same field in the 1980s. His wealth of experience and knowledge has shed valuable light upon the identity, function, meaning, and condition of the individual works in the Hendershott holdings of Pre-Columbian art. Dr. Robert Sonin's opinions on the gold works, in particular his views of the works from the Charles Craig estate, have been invaluable, as has the contribution of Stanley Guenter on the inscribed Maya jade pectoral.

In addition, Heritage Auction Galleries has benefited from the expertise of one of the foremost authorities on historic Native American art. Richard Pohrt, Jr., prepared the descriptions and analyses of the Native American artifacts belonging to Mr. Hendershott, and his writing will ensure the importance of this catalog for future generations of curators, collectors and students. In the case of the Meade ledger album, we have also benefited from the insights and perspective of Mike Cowdrey.

Heritage Auction Galleries has spared no effort in presenting the Hendershott Collection in the interest of serving a field of art and history about which so much remains to be written and known. As discoveries continue apace, we come to have a fuller understanding of the richness of the indigenous cultures of the Americas.

Edmund P. Pillsbury, Ph.D.
Chairman and Managing Director of Fine Arts
Heritage Auction Galleries

A NATIVE OF ARKANSAS, GARY HENDERSHOTT gained his love of collecting as most boys did, through the wonderful medium of stamps and coins.

"I started collecting in the 1950s when I was 8 years old," Hendershott said. "I would ride my bicycle to the 5 & Dime store to buy bags of assorted world stamps, plus I enlisted the help of a group of secretaries in downtown Little Rock who would save for me all the interesting stamps that crossed their desks. The weekly rounds I made on my bicycle to pick them up from their offices was a fondly-remembered pilgrimage. The very first coin I ever found was a large Greek silver piece in the alley behind my home. It was after WWII, and we had neighbors from all over Europe. One of them must have dropped this coin, which I still have in my collection."

"I became fascinated with the sense of history that stamps and coins presented to me," Hendershott said, "and that love of history has followed me through the years and through a number of different collections."

"Perhaps even more significantly," Hendershott remembered, "was finding my first arrowhead on our family farm in Arkansas. This was the start of my lifelong fascination with Native American artwork – an interest born, in part, of my own American Indian ancestry."

Years later, at the age of 18, Hendershott climbed the pyramid at Cobá, the tallest Mayan pyramid in existence, and watched the sunrise over the Yucatan and the Caribbean. "It was magnificent," Hendershott remembers, "and that was the beginning of my love affair with Pre-Columbian material."

Following that experience, Hendershott began buying pieces of

Pre-Columbian art at auction, building a collection that would be unrivaled in its scope and its depth. "This is an exceptionally pure artform," Hendershott said, "uninfluenced by European trends and styles. The people that made these magnificent pieces made them, and used them, for both daily and ceremonial use. This exquisite art was truly an indispensable part of their lives."

Currently, Gary's collecting passion is material related to Alexander the Great (356 - 323 B.C.). "By the age of 26, Alexander had conquered the entire known world," Hendershott said, "an unparalleled achievement in the annals of human history. He also facilitated the rise of Christianity, which came about through his One World, One Nation vision. I find him to be a fascinating figure, and one that I look forward to learning more about."

When asked why he chose to sell his impressive collection of Native American and Pre-Columbian art, Hendershott replied, "I have gone as far as I can go with this current collection within my means, and it's now time to let someone else take it to the next level. However, as my interests are still fairly broad, I'm also looking to build a comprehensive collection documenting the history of mankind, from 1000 BC to the present. I've already got a good start through coins, but now I'll be adding to it with artwork and other fascinating pieces."

"I'm proud to have been the temporary custodian of these great works of art," Hendershott said, "and I'm pleased that the next generation of collectors will cherish them as I have. The collecting world is a wonderful fraternity that I'm thrilled to be a part of, and I look forward to many more exciting adventures brought about by this wonderful hobby in the future."

Maya and Mesoamerica

47001

FIGURE OF A STANDING WOMAN

Maya, Jaina
A.D. 550–900
Ceramic, traces of original red paint
Height 10⅝ in. Width 4⅞ in.

Although mold–made, the details are unusually refined and sharp in this standing female figure. Her hands are held palms together in a respectful gesture and point upward to a well-rendered head pendant at the center of her bead necklace. Ear spools and multi-banded, segmented bracelets complete her jewelry. Her hair is cut in the notched fashion often seen in Maya female representations. A simple, long mantle covers her head and falls full-length at her back and sides. Her upper body is covered with a *huipil* shown as having a textured weave of squares centered with circles and its bottom edge rimmed by pom-poms. A three-part fringed garment hangs over her skirt from under the *huipil,* its punched patterning suggesting that it may have been a gauzy semi-openwork weave. A textured band finished in fringe is at the bottom of her skirt, from which her bare feet show. Other than several patches at the lower rear the overall condition is excellent.

Provenance
Sotheby's New York: sale 4749Y, December 1981, Lot 204
John-Platt Collection (Daniel M. Friedenberg)
Sotheby's New York: sale 7902, 15 May 2003, Lot 257, p.176

Published
Von Winning, Hasso, *The John-Platt Collection of Pre-Columbian Art.* Charlottesville: the University of Virginia Art Museum, 1986, p.67, Fig. 125

Estimate: $3,000-$5,000

47002

MALE FIGURE SEATED CROSS-LEGGED WITH FOLDED ARMS

Maya
A.D. 550–900
Ceramic, traces of paint
Height 7¼ in. Width 4⅛ in.

Seated cross-legged, this figure wears a now-incomplete large belt with rear-projecting jaguar head, which may originally have been a form of ballgame accoutrement. Beneath a bead necklace and atop the folded arms rests a broadly rendered horizontal celt-form pendant from which hangs a trefoil element. A bead flanked by loops bands each upper arm. The loincloth is non-symmetrically rendered, with the fringed frontal flap lying over the left thigh. At the rear, a tail-like element extends from beneath the jaguar head along the left buttock. Although damaged, the central element of the lower headdress band formed a five-point cosmological emblem. Behind this, an arched backing is bordered by beads, with a larger central one at top, and flattened tufts of feathers project outward above each of the wearer's ears. In addition to general surface abrasion, especially in the head and headdress area, small losses occur from headdress and kilt, with larger missing portions of the man's right foot, and a missing right ear of the jaguar head. Some traces of original paint remain.

Provenance
Skinner, Boston: sale 2209, 20 September 2003, Lot 56, pp.18-19

Estimate: $1,500-$2,000

47003

STANDING MALE DIGNITARY WITH FOLDED ARMS

Maya, Jaina
A.D. 550–900
Ceramic, traces of original paint
Height 6½ in. Width 2 in.

The long-kilted male figure stands with arms folded and feet thrust outward on a largely restored base. A thick belt is loop-tied in front. He wears a necklace of large beads and circular ear spools to each of which a large tear-shaped bead is attached. The slightly parted lips suggest a restrained smile. A puffy headdress is gathered part way up by a vertically-striated blue band. Several tubular elements, most with the ends broken, project from the top of the headdress. Other than the base area and the missing headdress components, the condition is good, with traces of original paint remaining.

Provenance
Stendahl Art Gallery, Los Angeles
Skinner, Boston: sale 2209, 20 September 2003, Lot 57, p.18-19

Estimate: $3,000-$4,000

47004

MASKED STANDING BALLPLAYER HOLDING A BALL

Maya, Jaina
A.D. 550–900
Buff Ceramic, traces of paint
Height 9¼ in. Width 5⅜ in.

The masked ballplayer stands with legs firmly placed somewhat apart, his left arm extended upward from the body and his balancing lowered right arm holding a ball with the hand. He wears only a loincloth with a flap at the left side and a leaf-shaped longer flap in front with simple incised markings. His upper thighs to either side have two rows of vertical gashes at front and sides, the upper row of which extends across the back just below the waist. A twisted band is at either wrist. Even more attention-commanding than the gesture is the grotesque mask, whose grimacing features include a flap-like beard that bears a crudely incised upside-down schematic face. Prominent, bulging eyes appear behind the mask, while within the large oval exposed mouth area appear what most resemble grinning vertically-scarified lips. Eight pointed elements radiate forward around the face, while the mask is topped by a large knot above the center of which rise four tubular shapes with cut upper edges. These latter extend upward to a length as high as the full head of the wearer. While the overall condition of the upper body is good, the lower half of the front loincloth flap is a replacement, as is most of the right leg and the left leg below the knee.

Provenance
Mr. & Mrs. Peter Wray Collection
Splendors of the World, Haiku, Hawaii

Estimate: $4,000-$6,000

47005

SEATED FIGURE WITH DEER HEADDRESS

Maya, Jaina
A.D. 550–900
Ceramic, traces of paint
Height 7½ in. Width 3½ in.

The male figure is shown seated cross-legged and wearing a kilt with wide belt. The belt includes a flap at the figure's right and one hanging in front over the legs. While the arms are folded near the torso, the man gestures outward from his mouth with the right hand, as though emphasizing a spoken point. A simple, cord-like necklace holds a large central bead. An exaggeratedly large deer head rests on a rolled cushion atop the man's head, with deer head angled sharply upward and the ears hanging behind the man's head. Since both deer ears are replacements, their size and shape are problematic. The front lower belt flap is considerably restored, and rear elements are missing from the necklace. Remains of red and original Maya blue paint are visible. The figure contains a still-functional whistle.

Provenance
Collection of Jay C. Leff
The John-Platt Collection (Daniel M. Friedenberg)
Sotheby's New York: sale 7902, 15 May 2003, Lot 255, p. 175

Published
Von Winning, Hasso, *The John-Platt Collection of Pre-Columbian Art,* Charlottesville: The University of Virginia Art Museum, 1986, p.67, Fig. 124
Sotheby Parke Bernet Auction Catalogue 4374, May 1980, Item 19

Exhibited
Carnegie Institute, Pittsburgh, October 1959 to January 1960, *Exotic Art from Ancient and Primitive Civilizations,* Collection of Jay C. Leff

Estimate: $4,000-$6,000

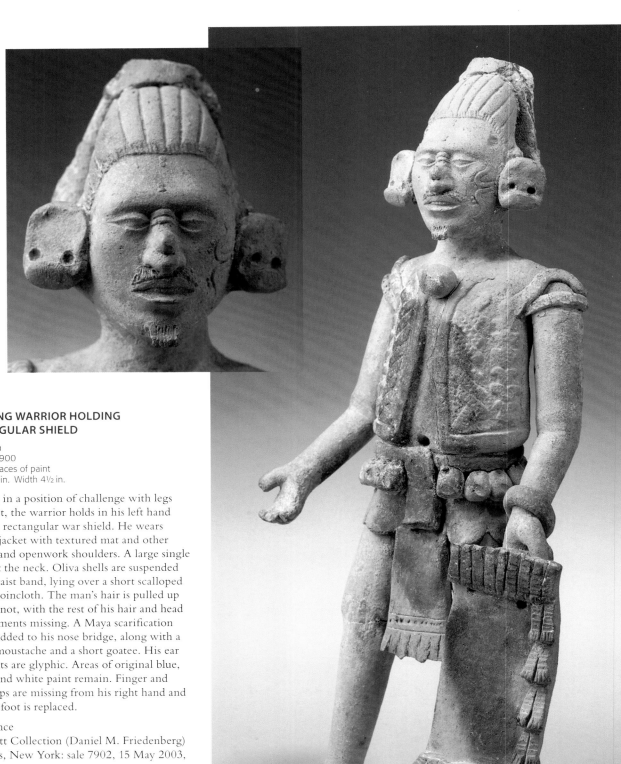

47006

STANDING WARRIOR HOLDING RECTANGULAR SHIELD

Maya, Jaina
A.D. 550–900
Ceramic, traces of paint
Height 9½ in. Width 4½ in.

Standing in a position of challenge with legs well apart, the warrior holds in his left hand a flexible rectangular war shield. He wears a bolero jacket with textured mat and other patterns and openwork shoulders. A large single bead is at the neck. Oliva shells are suspended from a waist band, lying over a short scalloped kilt and loincloth. The man's hair is pulled up to a topknot, with the rest of his hair and head accoutrements missing. A Maya scarification knob is added to his nose bridge, along with a clipped moustache and a short goatee. His ear ornaments are glyphic. Areas of original blue, yellow, and white paint remain. Finger and thumb tips are missing from his right hand and his right foot is replaced.

Provenance
John-Platt Collection (Daniel M. Friedenberg)
Sotheby's, New York: sale 7902, 15 May 2003, Lot 254, p.175

Published
Von Winning, Hasso, *The John-Platt Collection of Pre-Columbian Art,*Charlottesville: The University of Virginia Art Museum. 1986, p. 66, Fig. 123

Estimate: $6,000-$10,000

47007

STANDING MALE FIGURE WITH LEFT HAND ON RIGHT WRIST

Maya, Jaina
A.D. 550–900
Ceramic, traces of original paint
Height 8 in. Width 2⅝ in.

The figure stands stiffly on long-calved legs, looking straight forward with an almost blank stare. His left hand rests lightly on his right at waist level where the bent arms meet. He wears what may have been a short sleeveless tunic gathered at the waist by a wide belt with a flap folded to extend downward at front center almost to the knees. The lower edge of the tunic was cut at several points to allow ease of movement. Circular appliqué tabs decorate both front and back of the tunic, over which a large coil-form necklace supports a concave circular piece, which once had something attached at its center. He wears two-part ear spools, and a stocking-cap-like head covering secured by a band tied at back. An element that once capped the head covering is broken away.

Delicate and finely rendered facial tattooing is of special interest. A possible inward-facing but simplified serpent head marks either temple-cheekbone area, while a skeletal jaw complete with articulation points and teeth, is defined along either jaw.

Overall condition is good, with considerable remaining post-firing Maya blue and white paint. There are metallic deposits on the back.

Provenance
Sotheby's New York: sale 7900, 15 May 2003, Lot 256, p.175

Estimate: $6,000-$10,000

47008

TRIPOD PLATE SHOWING A SEATED LORD IN ITS CENTRAL MEDALLION

Maya
A.D. 550–800
Polychrome ceramic
Diameter 14 in.

As one looks down onto this well-preserved tripod plate, a lord facing and gesturing to his right is shown seated cross-legged on a throne. There is a large cushion at his left, which may be making visually explicit an actual throne back. The tall, freely painted headdress shows a grinning, large-eyed deity mask with an upward-curving snout. Feathers turn back and down from the top of the headdress. On the sloping vessel wall four profile stylized cormorants, all facing in the same direction the lord looks, are separated by vertical dividers. On the exterior there is a repeated series of diagonal I-shaped bands, and the tripod legs have three horizontal black stripes. The plate is in the Holmul area painting style, which utilizes subtly nuanced tones of red slip to realize the images (Dorie Reents-Budet. *Painting the Maya Universe: Royal Ceramics of the Classic Period.* Durham and London: Duke University Press,1994, pp.180 ff.). Clay rattles remain in the hollow legs. There are some root marks, along with a small rim chip on the underside.

Provenance
Christie's, Paris: sale 5057, 12 June 2003: Lot 622, p. 184

Estimate: $10,000-$14,000

47009

PAINTED BOWL

Maya, Ulua Region
A.D. 700–850
Polychrome ceramic
Height 5⅞ in. Width 7⅜ in.

This tall-sided bowl is lavishly painted on almost every available surface, both inside and out. The dense decoration painted in black, red, and orange is in the distinctive late style of the Ulua region of Honduras. Qualitatively, this vessel is at the highest end of the Ulua region continuum in image formation, surface arrangement, and execution. The principal design, on the larger rounded lower section, repeats the same motif three times. In each unit a seated figure in elaborate regalia faces a large black circular form, the latter bearing what appears to be a complex deity mask done in cream-colored slip (age erosion makes this image very difficult to read with certainty). Each black circle has slightly different bordering decoration, all comprised of feathers and fabric elements. These latter suggest that this represents an altar, though probably one with direct reference to the ritual ballgame. The primarily black body paint of the seated figures can be related to three contexts: war, the ballgame, and merchants, the latter also at times serving as spy-ambassadors.

Five monstrous profile heads are painted on the more vertical upper section, their nose and ear ornaments and headdress elements all carefully delineated. Broad red and narrow black bands separate the upper and lower exterior fields, and a red rim above a black line completes the exterior. On the inside upper section thirteen vertically-oriented profile crocodile-like heads with snouts touching the rim are aligned. Below double black bands three broader red bands cover the inside of the bowl proper. Lighter-toned alternating simple linear shapes punctuate the wider central band. Even the exterior base of the bowl is painted with concentric black and red circles. The bowl is complete, with one major crack reglued with minor inpainting. There is slight surface abrasion and paint loss.

Provenance
Dave DeRoche, Piedmont, California

Estimate: $1,500-$2,000

47010

OPENWORK PECTORAL OF TWO FACING DIGNITARIES

Maya
A.D. 550–800
Shell
Height 2⅞ in. Width 3¹⁵/₁₆ in.

The frequency with which Maya pectorals in pale-colored shell have openwork areas suggests that they may have been conceived for use against a material of stronger color. Only then would the silhouetting of image have achieved full impact. For this case, all of the solid elements of the pectoral combine to suggest a large-eyed, agnathic frontal face. This is enhanced by the finely incised double lines at the arched lower edge which define three lobed forms, the middle one having a slight downward dip at its center which reinforces the suggestion of a nose seen frontally.

The solid forms show two male profiles facing inward toward one another, with a column separating them. Fine encircling incised outlines indicate that the heads appear behind a front plane, as though seen inside the eyes of the mask.

There are various chips along the edges, the center bar was broken at top and bottom and has been reglued, and there are old breaks at the right and left ends, with resulting missing parts. There are dirt encrustations and stains on the back.

Provenance
Bonhams & Butterfields, San Francisco: sale 7546E, 14 June 2004, lot 1033, p. 11 (Property from the Tara Colburn Estate, Los Angeles)

Estimate: $3,000-$4,000

47011

FACE MASK

Maya (Pre-Classic or Early Classic)
A.D. 250–550
Black stone, traces of red pigment
Height 5⅝ in. Width 4⅝ in.

The size and weight of this black stone mask suggest that it was either for a royal belt or to be tied to a shrine effigy. The ambiguous iconography and the uncertain treatment of the mouth scrolls both suggest a relatively early date, perhaps even before the Early Classic was under way. Traces remain of red pigment which once covered the mask. There are a number of small natural flaws in the stone, and the center of the back has old vertical scratches.

Provenance
Dylan Graeme
Dr. Wally and Brenda Zollman, Indianapolis
Butterfields & Butterfields, San Francisco: sale 7307E, 25 March 2002, lot 5110, p.32, ill. p.32

Estimate: $5,000-$7,000

47012

PENDANT OF AN ENTHRONED KING

Maya
A.D. 550–800
Jadeite, Weight 98 grams
Height 3¾ in. Width 2⅛ in.

Roughly long oval in outline, this thin jadeite pendant shows an enthroned king viewed from the front. The requirements of jade-working technique force a number of simplifications which challenge interpretation. However, the strongest probability is that the ruler cradles in his arms an arched vision-serpent bar, below which is visible a double-band belt having a central emblem and bordered by pendant oliva shells. Hanging between the parted legs is the ruler's elaborate breechcloth. The headdress shows a frontal animal head with bared teeth and the curled eyes associated with several deities. Above this head feathers fan out from a central circular medallion. Three-part ear spools, a necklace, bracelets, and anklets complete the royal Maya regalia.

Seen from the side, it is apparent that the ancient artist carefully selected a bright green jadeite layer lying atop a duller brownish-green layer; shallow saw marks suggest that he considered trying to separate this brighter layer from the rest, but rejected the idea. The piece is drilled through from side to side and from top to bottom.

Provenance
Peter Wright, Florida (acquired 1970)
Daniel M. Friedenburg Collection
Sotheby's, New York: sale 7902, 15 May 2003, lot 298, p.192

Estimate: $4,000-$6,000

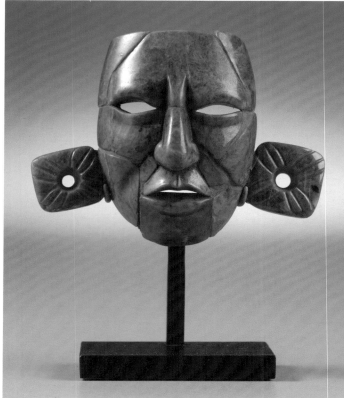

47013

MOSAIC PORTRAIT MASKETTE

Maya
A.D. 600–800
Jadeite, Weight 58 grams
Height 2⁵⁄₁₆ in. Width 3¹⁄₁₆ in.

Among the Maya portrait masks in sizes ranging from life-sized to miniature were constructed on wood matrices as mosaics comprised of jadeite and other valued and beautiful materials. Many of these, such as this splendid example, are vividly portrait-like. Life-sized masks found in several excavated burials confirm the portrait intent for those examples. Though small, the present mask projects vital energy, as well as being made up of particularly carefully shaped and fitted individual pieces. One cannot help noticing a tantalizing resemblance to the famous life-sized mask from Pakal's tomb at Palenque. Though reassembled on a modern backing, the condition of the all original components is excellent.

Provenance
Murray Korda, Orwell, Vermont
Splendors of the World, Haiku, Hawaii

Estimate: $20,000-$25,000

47014

HEAD-FORM PENDANT OF SEATED DIGNITARY

Maya
A.D. 550–800
Jadeite, Weight 146 grams
Height 2⅞ in. Width 2⅛ in.

This pendant of an ear-spooled dignitary wearing a feline headdress is unusually well developed sculpturally, utilizing the entire jadeite pebble to contribute to the space-occupying substantiality of the image. While the man's facial features are conventionalized, the headdress animal is developed into actively energized forms. In the animal's right eye area, the maker apparently encountered an inclusion or anomaly in the jadeite which forced him to re-drill and thus overly enlarge the eye. This symmetry-destroying "recovery" adds to the overall animation of the headdress. The condition is very good, with a horizontal suspension hole drilled through one inch from the top.

Provenance
The Bogousslavsky Collection
Sotheby's New York: 4 December 1981, lot 75
John-Platt Collection (Daniel M. Friedenberg)
Sotheby's New York: sale 7902, 15 May 2003, lot 299, p.192

Publication
Von Winning, Hasso, *The John Platt Collection of Pre-Columbian Art,* Charlottesville, The University of Virginia Art Museum, 1986, fig. 171, pp. 85-86

Estimate: $3,000-$4,000

47015

PENDANT DEPICTING A HALF-FIGURE WEARING A FELINE HEADDRESS

Maya
A.D. 550–800
Jadeite, Weight 128 grams
Height 3⅞ in. Width 2⅜ in.

The irregularly-shaped, relatively flat jadeite pendant has a low relief representation of a male half-figure wearing a feline headdress that appears to engulf the wearer's head within its open mouth. The animal is most likely to be a jaguar, a frequent *way* (spirit companion) of kings. Below the headdress ear spools are visible. The man's right arm rests against the chest along a belt, with the open-handed left arm diagonally above it so that the hand is below his chin. The jadeite's primary color is a light apple green, with some brownish and grayish mottling. Condition is very good, with diagonally drilled holes running from side to back at either side of the pendant.

Provenance
The Bogousslavsky Collection
Sotheby's, New York: 4 December 1981, lot 71
John-Platt Collection (Daniel M Friedenberg)
Sotheby's, New York: sale 7902, 23 May 2003, lot 298, p.192

Published
Von Winning, Hasso, *The John-Platt Collection of Pre-Columbian Art,* Charlottesville: The University of Virginia Art Museum, 1986, fig.170, p.85

Estimate: $4,000-$6,000

47016

SET OF FOUR PENDANTS: FRONTAL FACES WITH HEADDRESSES

Maya
A.D. 600–800
Jadeite, red pigment
(A) Height 2⁷/₁₆ in.   Width 2¼ in.
(B) Height 3⅛ in.   Width 2¾ in.
(C) Height 3⅛ in.   Width 2⁹/₁₆ in.
(D) Height 2¹³/₁₆ in.   Width 2¹/₁₆ in.

These four closely similar pendants are cut from the same cobble of jadeite and can, exercising some ingenuity, be fit together sequentially from A to D as listed above. It is most unusual to have an original group worked from a single piece of jadeite still together after over 1250 years. All show a frontal face with headdress, earspools, and necklace. The headdresses of pendants B, C, and D have the conventional representation of a jaguar, seen as engulfing the wearer's face in its maw. The headdress of pendant A shows a central, vertically-oriented long oval element, from which two scroll forms issue to either side. This personage also wears a necklace of round beads. The other three show variants of necklaces based on a central medallion flanked by scrolls. Each pendant is drilled for suspension near the top diagonally from the side to the back. All four pendants were rubbed all over with a red mineral pigment (almost certainly cinnabar), a considerable amount of which remains, especially in the deeper cuts. The condition of all four is excellent.

Provenance
Enrique Vargas, San José, Costa Rica
Richard Sirkin, M.D., Buffalo, New York
David Walley, Pontotoc, Mississippi

Estimate: $12,000-$18,000

47017

PECTORAL DEPICTING TWO ENTHRONED DEITIES

Maya
A.D. 700–800
Jadeite
Height 4¼ in. Width 3⅞ in.

Commentary on a Late Classic Maya Jade Plaque by Stanley Paul Guenter

This carved jade has previously been commented upon by Robert Sonin and Dieter Dütting. Stylistically, both in regards to the figural scene on the front and the inscription on the reverse, the carving dates to the latter part of the Late Classic period, almost certainly to the eighth century A.D. The carving on the face of the object depicts two Maya individuals in profile, facing each other. Each figure is seated upon a throne. The left hand figure sits on a throne upon which are carved two human faces shown frontally. From each of the heads hang four long rectangular shapes, possibly portraying the celts that often hung from belt heads in typical Maya royal costume. The right hand figure sits atop a *witz* monster, emblem of stone and mountains. The *witz* monster faces to the left, and is distinguished by a lack of a lower jaw, very large eye, and a broad upper part of the head marked by a number of engraved circles. Between the two throne supports kneels a hunchbacked dwarf, the common companion of the Maize god or of Maya kings impersonating this deity.

The figure to the left is actually the Maize God himself, identified by the corn foliage that sprouts from his head and droops both behind his head and in front of his face. The figure holds his left hand elegantly over his chest, while his right hand rests comfortably on his thigh. This gesture has been identified as one expressed by the focal person in scenes on Maya pottery vessels (Patricia Ancona-Ha, Jorge Pérez de Lara, and Mark Van Stone, "Some Observations on Hand Gestures in Maya Art" in *The Maya Vase Book Volume 6*, pp. 1072-1089, edited by Barbara and Justin Kerr. New York: Kerr Associates, 2000). This Maize God faces and leans toward the figure on the right, who can be identified as the Chocolate God by virtue of the cacao pods that hang from the strands of his hair. This Chocolate God rests his left hand on his own thigh while raising his right hand, palm outstretched, toward the Maize God in a gesture that has been interpreted as a greeting (ibid: 1080).

Our knowledge of the Chocolate God has increased considerably over the last few years and this jade plaque adds to that knowledge in a significant way. The iconography of the Maize and Chocolate Gods overlaps considerably, which is understandable in that cacao pods and maize cobs, unlike most vegetables, grow directly off the plant stalk or tree trunk. Corn kernels and cacao beans grow in rows very similar to each other and, as scholar Simon Martin has noted, these plants and their associated gods are intimately related. This led Martin and associate Mary Miller (Mary Miller and Simon Martin, p.63, *Courtly Art of the Ancient Maya*. New York: Thames and Hudson, 2004) to propose that the Chocolate God could have either been

an aspect of the Maize God or possibly his brother, not enough evidence existing to favor one or the other of these possibilities. This jade plaque, portraying both of these gods interacting, thus provides unique and strong evidence suggesting that the Maize and Chocolate Gods were separate entities, possibly brothers as Miller and Martin have suggested, and not merely aspects of the same deity.

The back of this jade plaque carries a short three hieroglyph inscription. This inscription was first analyzed by Dieter Dütting (Hasso von Winning, *The John-Platt Collection of Pre-Columbian Art*, Charlottesville: University of Virginia Art Museum,1986, catalogue no. 166), but advances in the decipherment of ancient Maya texts which have occurred since then make a reanalysis necessary. These hieroglyphs, following Dütting's original analysis, will be designated A, B, and C. In the following table the first column provides the "T numbers" for identifying Maya hieroglyphs first proposed by J. Eric S. Thompson (J. Eric S.Thompson. *A Catalog of Maya Hieroglyphs*. Norman: University of Oklahoma Press, 1962). The second column provides a phonetic transcription of each of these signs.

Below follow a transcription and transliteration of the text.

Table 1

Hieroglyph	T#	Phonetic Value
A	61.534.2	*yu-la-li*
B	204.102.1000b	*u-ki-na*
C	12.99.502,142	*AJ-o-ma-ma*

Transliteration: *y-ulaal ukiin aj-omam*
Translation: "the *ulaal* of *Ukiin*, He of Oman."

This short text, as with many similar Maya texts, appears to be a "nametag," identifying the object upon which it was inscribed as belonging to a specific individual. The initial *y-* is the ergative possessive in Maya language, and the possessed object is said to be an *ulaal,* a word that is otherwise unattested in Classic Maya inscriptions. This word cannot be identified in Maya dictionaries and appears to have disappeared from modern Maya languages. However, by way of comparison with similar nametag texts the *ulaal* should refer to this jade plaque or the category of object (e.g.: pectoral, jewel, jade object, etc.) to which it belongs.

This *ulaal* belonged to an individual whose name and title appear in the next two hieroglyphs, Glyphs B and C. The personal name of the individual appears in Glyph B, which is phonetically spelled out as *Ukiin.* His title follows in Glyph C, and reads *Aj Omam,* or "He of *Omam,*" where *Omam* is most likely a toponym, or name of the ancient Maya site where *Ukiin* came from. Unfortunately, this is the only reference to *Omam* in the corpus of Maya hieroglyphic inscriptions and so the whereabouts of this site remain unknown. The style of the hieroglyphs and carving suggest that wherever *Omam* was located, it was somewhere within the Southern Maya Lowlands, which cover the modern country of Belize, the Petén district of Guatemala, eastern Tabasco and Chiapas states and southern Campeche and Quintana Roo states in Mexico.

It can thus be seen that this jade plaque bears an important image and text that help reveal the relationship of two primary Maya deities, as well as providing unique references to an otherwise unrecorded type of object (*ulaal*) and an otherwise unrecorded individual (*Ukiin*) from an otherwise unrecorded ancient Maya site (*Omam*).

Bibliography

Ancona-Ha, Particia, Jorge Pérez de Lara, and Mark Van Stone. "Some Observations on Hand Gestures in Maya Art." in *The Maya Vase Book Volume 6,* edited by Barbara and Justin Kerr. pp.1072-1089, New York: Kerr Associates, 2000.

Miller, Mary, and Simon Martin. *Courtly Art of the Ancient Maya.* New York: Thames and Hudson, 2004.

Thompson, J. Eric S. *A Catalog of Maya Hieroglyphs.* Norman: University of Oklahoma Press, 1962.

Von Winning, Hasso. *The John-Platt Collection of Pre-Columbian Art.* Charlottesville, Virginia: University of Virginia Art Museum, 1986.

A number of areas have been drilled in different ways. The most remarkable is a filament-thin drilled passage horizontally across the entire upper pectoral approximately one inch below the top. Clearly visible across the top is a deep horizontal slot, possibly remaining from a previous suspension channel when the pectoral slab was thicker. The edges of this slot have been softened with polishing. Inside this slot two small holes are drilled through from front to back a short distance from either end. Across the bottom three evenly-spaced fine drillings were started but were never completed all the way through the jadeite. At the lower proper left side one minute hole goes through and at the proper right two pass through. From the back it can be seen that two more side drills were started near the bottom but were not completed. The condition is excellent.

The lot is sold with copies of all supporting documentation.

Provenance
John-Platt Collection (Daniel M. Friedenberg)
Sotheby's, New York: sale 7902, 15 May 2003, lot 252, p.173

Publication
Von Winning, Hasso, *The John-Platt Collection of Pre-Columbian Art,* Charlottesville: The University of Virginia Art Museum, 1986. Ill. title page (in color); p.84, fig.166; ill. p.25 (drawing of glyphs on back)

Estimate: $40,000-$60,000

47018

FACE PANEL

Teotihuacan
A.D. 300–600
Alabaster with red pigment
Height 4¾ in. Width 3⅞ in.

A less than life-sized face panel of typical Teotihacan type, this alabaster example has residues of possibly several layers of overpainting, which suggests its use on more than one occasion. Three drilled holes on each side would have allowed the panel to be attached to other objects or to have decorative elements added. Both eyes and mouth show evidence of inlays, with magnification indicating tooth-shaped impressions at the proper left of the mouth. Such smaller-sized face panels may have had a range of ritual uses, from forming a component of more complex cosmological configurations to forming a part of the accoutrements of deity effigies. The condition is excellent: the words "Xultepec Guer. Mx. / Teo IV" appear on the back.

Provenance
David Walley, Pontotoc, Mississippi

Estimate: $4,000-$6,000

47019

STANDING DIGNITARY

Teotihuacan
A.D. 300–600
Green stone
Height 5⅜ in. Width 2 in.

A rather simplified representation of a fully clothed standing figure with plain, banded headdress, this image in dark green stone is relatively thin and flat. As represented, both upper and lower garments suggest female clothing, and their effect does relate to published representations considered to be female figures (Kathleen Berrin and Esther Pasztory, eds. *Teotihuacan Art from the City of the Gods*. London: Thames and Hudson, 1993, p.179, no.16). The condition is good, with small chips at top and some material missing at the rear of the proper right foot. "Teo. KK-H7" appears on the back of the figure.

Provenance
David Walley, Pontotoc, Mississippi

Estimate: $3,000-$4,000

47020

STANDING DIGNITARY WITH BIRD-FORM HEADDRESS

Guerrero
200 B.C.–A.D. 600
Green stone (serpentine?) with traces of red pigment,
Weight 1.57 kg.
Height 14½ in. Width 4³⁄₁₆ in.

The tall, frontally-viewed figure is shown with a trapezoidal face with flanges. Features are schematic. The combined size of the headdress with its opposing bird heads balances the facial area. The rectangular upper body terminates in clasped hands with the fingers delineated. His short, separated legs end in feet with visible toes.

As with so many of the stone figures from Guerrero this large example defies stylistic or cultural designation. The extraordinary range of parallel figures and masks found in the many cached deposits at the Aztec Templo Mayor may only serve to add complication, since they also have neither provenance nor chronological associations from their times and places of origin. The figure is in excellent condition, with some fine surface scratches.

Provenance
John-Platt Collection (Daniel M. Friedenberg)
Splendors of the World, Haiku, Hawaii

Publication
Von Winning, Hasso, *The John-Platt Pre-Columbian Collection*. Charlottesville: The University of Virginia Art Museum, 1986, p. 48, fig. 56.

Estimate: $10,000-$15,000

47021

LARGE STYLIZED HEAD

Mezcala
300 B.C.–A.D. 300
Green stone
Height 4⅞ in. Width 4⅜ in.

Within the overall trapezoidal head shape a bold series of grooves defines the basic facial features, as well as separating ear–area flanges and defining a band along the top of the head. The eye areas are rather deeply hollowed, which combines with unusually explicit lower lip definition to give a degree of liveliness not common in Mezcala images.

Such elegantly simplified heads, and the related full figures, have long appealed to collectors whose eyes were in part schooled by twentieth-century abstraction. As with many examples, this one was drilled at center top for attachment. The large size and weight of this example suggest that it was not worn, however. The head is in excellent condition, with scattered mineralized deposits visible under magnification. Written in black on the back is "Mezcala. Balsas R. Guerrero.M."

Provenance
David Walley, Pontotoc, Mississippi

Estimate: $5,000-$7,000

47022

CIRCULAR FACE MASK WITH EARS

Tlatilco
1100 – 900 B.C.
Ceramic, traces of paint
Height 5¼ in. Width 5¼ in.

The round face with open eyes, mouth, and nostrils is surrounded by a flange behind the facial plane. Three holes are punched, one at top, and one at either temple, so that the mask could be worn. Surviving Tlatilco figurines (Michael D. Coe. *The Jaguar's Children: Pre-Classic Central Mexico.* New York: The Museum of Primitive Art, 1965: figs.123, 147, 157, 158) show such masks being worn by ball players and figures clothed to suggest a shaman (Coe 1965 also illustrates a closely similar round, flanged mask, no. 165). The mask is in good condition, with some root marks, light mineral deposits, and a minor age crack running outward from the proper left eye through the suspension hole to the rim. Some red and yellow paint remains on the face.

Provenance
Skinner, Boston: sale 2209, 20 September 2003, Lot 61, pp. 18–19

Estimate: $200-$300

47023

MASKED DANCER

Colima
200 B.C.–A.D. 200
Buff ceramic
Height 10½ in. Width 4 in.

A number of Colima figures of this exact iconography are known, including a large example in the Dallas Museum of Art. The costumed dancer wears a mask having a large, strongly projecting squared snout with prominent fanglike teeth. The nose is tipped by pointed, upthrust elements. A strap-held helmet develops into a large circular feathered fan not unlike headdresses worn by contemporary *quetzales* dancers of southeast Mexico. A two-part tailpiece fans rearward from the broad waist belt, balanced in front by a triangular flap. Crossed bands on the torso and double banding of the arms and legs complete the costume. The outstretched arms end in hands clasping four-part flexible dance wands, the right one missing and the left reglued. A whistle is incorporated in the head, with the mouthpiece where a right ear would be. The rear flap was broken off halfway down and has been reglued. Other than minor stains and chips, the condition is good.

Provenance
Dave DeRoche, Piedmont, California

Estimate: $1,800-$2,400

47024

TWO ARTICULATED FIGURES (A,B)

Teotihuacan
A.D. 300–600
Ceramic (A,B), traces of original paint (B)
(A) Height 4⅝ in.
(B) Height 6½ in.

Both articulated figures are comprised of five parts, which were intended to be joined by tying: a head and torso unit and separate arms and legs. The smaller figure has a cleft head, ear spools and a necklace, with bracelets on both arms. The larger figure has a three-part headdress, more elaborate ear spools with four-petaled flower centers, and a necklace. The torso of the larger figure is developed anatomically to indicate the rib cage. All components of both figures are in good condition, with the larger having residues of red and yellow paint, a small chip at the proper left shoulder, and a missing proper left thumb. Mist spraying of both figures resulted in uniform drying speed of all parts, suggesting that in both cases the parts belong together.

An articulated figure of which the head-torso unit appears to be from the same mold as the larger figure here is illustrated in Kathleen Berrin and Esther Pasztory, eds. *Teotihuacan Art from the City of the Gods.* London: Thames and Hudson, 1993, p.234, no.104, right figure.

Provenance
Skinner, Boston: sale 2209, 20 September 2003: lot 23 (ill. p.12)

Estimate: $3,000-$4,000

47025

DOUBLE-CHAMBERED FLUTE WITH HEAD OF AN OLD PERSON WITH BALLOON-LIKE BREASTS

Veracruz
A.D. 300–600
Buff ceramic
Height 7⅝ in. Width 3⅞ in.

Although mold-made, this head of a very old person is fully detailed and expressive, the overall network of wrinkles carefully shown. A non-symmetrical headdress has an arrangement of four feathers toward its left. This is balanced at its right by a vividly rendered hummingbird-like avian thrusting its beak into the headdress proper. A band of appliquéd disks joins the two side elements across the top of the headdress. Large ear spools complete the figure's décor. Coils of clay were attached at the outside of either flute barrel to suggest shoulders and arms. The image is completed by pendulous, balloon-like breasts. The two flute barrels, joined near the end, further the suggestion of a full figure. Each barrel has three finger holes.

The large number of surviving examples, plus the considerable typological complexity of some, suggest that music was a central and highly developed component of ancient Veracruz ritual performance. The use of flutes with hand drums, some played at the same time by one performer, survives today among a number of Middle American groups.

The flute was found broken into several pieces. These have been reglued with replacement material, except for the breasts, which are largely rebuilt.

Provenance
Collection of Stanley Marcus, Dallas
Collection of Paul L. and Alice C. Baker, Tuscon, Arizona
Bonhams & Butterfields, San Francisco: sale 7594E, 6 December 2004, Lot 1520, p.150

Publications
Jane Stevenson Day, PH.D, *Precolumbian Art From the Collection of Paul L. and Alice C. Baker,* Tucson, Tucson Museum of Art, 1996, ill. p.79, fig.87

Estimate: $2,000-$3,000

47026

STANDING FIGURE WHO GRASPS A POLE AND HAS AN ELABORATE REMOVABLE HEADDRESS

Veracruz, central area (?)
A.D. 300–700
Buff ceramic
Height 10⅜ in. Width 3¹⁵⁄₁₆ in.

The figure stands grasping with both hands a pole which abuts the toes of his right foot and slopes slightly outward from the vertical. The head is enlarged and squared off at top to provide support for the removable headdress. His mouth has an everted upper lip which reveals filed upper teeth, which form a T-shape. Large leaf-shaped tabs attached at each ear lobe probably represent some flexible material. A scarf is around the man's neck, knotted almost like a neck tie to give a large tab which covers the chest. At the abdomen two large knotted units are placed one above the other from which two fringed tabs fall to the knees. A kilt completes the figure's dress. The large horizontally-oriented center band of the kilt has a low relief representation of a Tajín-derived profile serpent head facing toward the proper right. In the upper right corner of this band the Maya Venus sign appears. The elaborate removable headdress has an overall shape reminiscent of a shako, complete with chin strap. As visible from the front, a broad, flat-looped piece rises vertically at rear center. Below this, five horizontal bands form the headdress proper. Each is composed of center and side-termination puffs (probably cotton but possibly downy feathers) between which are placed elaborate knots. Three pairs of punched holes near the bottom would have allowed the headdress to be tied firmly to the main figure. The overall condition is good, with scattered surface mineral deposits. Various breaks have been repaired, with more of these in the headdress, on which the lowest rear horizontal band at the proper left is a modern replacement.

Provenance
Bonhams & Butterfields, San Francisco: sale 7477E, 8 December 2003, p.11, lot 3019

Estimate: $3,500-$4,500

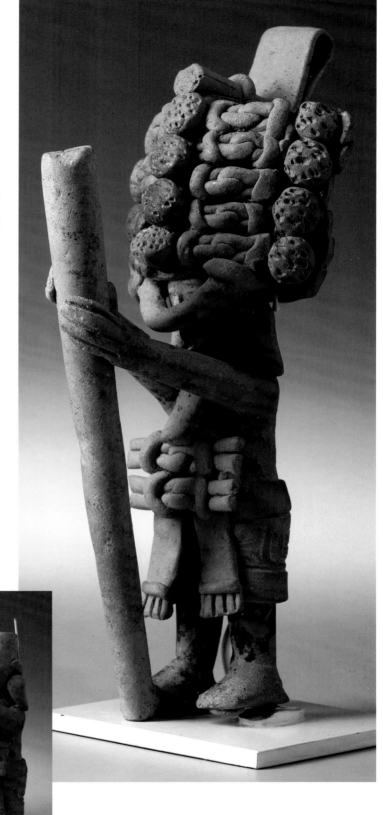

47027

SEATED FEMALE FIGURE

Veracruz, central area
A.D. 300–700
Ceramic, burnished buff slip, natural bitumen paint
Height 14 in. Width 8½ in.

This frontal female figure is seated cross-legged and wearing a skirt which is now partially broken away along its front hem. Her slightly arched hands, the fingers and fingernails of the right hand delineated with exceptional attentiveness, rest lightly on the knee and ankle of her left leg, which rests atop the right leg. Her large head is vibrantly rendered, with open eyes, the mouth slightly open as though producing a sound, and an overall portrait-like quality. Her banded headdress has a chin strap and side panels toward the rear, with prominent spool forms at either side of the forehead band. She wears medium-sized ear spools and a simple necklace band with one central, front bead. The pupils of her eyes are formed of attached, flattened balls that are accented with the black natural bitumen pigment characteristic of the region. Her face and upper body are covered with a rich, burnished cream slip, much of which remains.

A number of missing components have been given modern replacements: the proper right headdress spool; much of the proper left hand; toes and ball of the proper right foot; and proper right thumb. Reglued areas include some further patching, most in unimportant areas.

Provenance
Bonhams & Butterfields, San Francisco: sale 7477E, 8 December 2003, p.10, ill. p.10

Estimate: $4,000-$6,000

47028

SEATED CROSS-LEGGED FIGURE

Veracruz, central area
A.D. 300 – 700
Ceramic, traces of paint
Height 7¾ in. Width 6 in.

The seated, cross-legged figure has its hands resting on either knee. The head is bare, the eyes open with appliquéd pupils, and the open mouth shows filed teeth, leaving the two central ones in a somewhat-eroded T-shape. Elongated ears were punched to receive ear spools, and four medium-sized holes running from front to back on the center axis of the skull were probably intended for added head decoration or a headdress. There are simple armbands at the elbows, and a hastily-modeled larger band around the mid-chest, with a barely-suggested horizontally-oriented face at the front center. The waist is encircled by a band, to which a modern loin-cloth flap has been added at the front. The condition is otherwise good, with scattered surface mineral deposits and considerable original red paint on his face.

Provenance
Bonhams & Butterfields, San Francisco: sale 7477E, 8 December 2003, Lot 3018, p.11, ill. p.10

Estimate: $3,000-$4,000

47029

STANDING MALE FIGURE WITH CONICAL HEADDRESS AND HANDS CLASPED IN FRONT OF FACE

Veracruz
A.D. 300–900
Ceramic, traces of original red paint
Height 25 in. Width 8 in.

The tall, rather narrowly-proportioned figure stands straight with his arms raised so that the hands meet in front of the chin as if in prayer, the left hand inside the right. Other than the headdress and elaborate ear spools, he is dressed with a necklace, a cape which falls to a rounded tip in back, three bracelets on each arm, a loincloth, and sandals with knots in front. The large conical headdress has a broad bottom band and is attached by a wide chin strap. A small double component hangs on the back of the conical element. The circular ear ornaments have long tubular projections thrusting forward.

Rather extensive breakage has been consolidated and repaired. There is a thermoluminescence report from Laboratory Ralf Kotalla (No. 07220303) indicating firing 1200 years before present with a 20% variable. A copy of this report will be available for inspection.

Provenance
Mr. Calderon, Los Angeles
Splendors of the World, Haiku, Hawaii

Estimate: $8,000-$12,000

47030

HEAD OF EAGLE WARRIOR

Veracruz
A.D. 300–700
Ceramic, traces of red paint
Height 11½ in. Width 9¼ in.

This life-sized head was once part of a full figure. The youthful face is vibrantly rendered with a candid expression and slightly parted lips. In addition to large circular ear spools, the figure wears an eagle warrior's helmet in which his face emerges from the bird's open beak. The raptor's eyes, beak, and feathers are all rendered in appliquéd relief.

Much of the ceramic sculpture from central Veracruz which has been found in archaeological contexts is in large groups, all of which were ritually broken as a part of their ceremonial use. Figures in these groupings cover a considerable range of sizes and gestural configurations. Thus far it has been difficult to assign specific types to roles within the ceremonial activities. The condition is very good, with some tips missing from the feathers of the eagle headdress.

Provenance
Splendors of the World, Haiku, Hawaii

Estimate: $4,000-$5,000

47031

STANDING MALE FIGURE WITH HIS RIGHT HAND TO HIS SMILING MOUTH

Veracruz
A.D. 300–700
Ceramic, traces of original paint
Height 20 in. Width 10½ in.

The basically naked male figure stands with legs slightly spread, his left arm away from his side with forearm raised and hand held palm outward with fingers and thumb extended. He holds his right hand, to which a wristband attaches a short horn-like object, to the corner of his open mouth. His flattened head is trapezoidal, with the typical Veracruz turban-like head covering. Leaf-shaped tabs attached to his earlobes may represent some flexible material. His facial expression is bemused rather than broadly smiling. A bordered band binds his torso below a double-strand bead necklace with a simple, schematic central face pendant. The middle of the chest band shows intertwined, scrolling patterns at the center of which may be simplified, perhaps misunderstood components of a profile serpent head. His turban is centered with a symmetrical serpent-derived eye-cheek combination, flanked at either side just outside four ascending holes by profile serpent heads which face outward at an angle toward the upper headdress corners. Scrolls ripple along the top. The figure has been reassembled from several relatively large components, but with very little replacement. The entire surface has a consistent patination of root marks and mineral deposits, along with traces of original paint.

Provenance
Skinner, Boston: sale 2209, 20 September 2003, Lot 48, p.17

Estimate: $6,000-$9,000

47032

URN WITH SEATED DEITY

Zapotec
A.D. 550–850
Ceramic, traces of original paint
Height 12⅜ in. Width 11 in.

An elaborate headdress commands over half of the visual space in this representation of a deity seated cross-legged in front of a cylindrical urn, which the image conceals from view. A flared headdress of feathers rises above a central glyph; these together form the focal center of the headdress. To each side, at glyph-level, tabs ending in eyes are completed by outward-spreading feathers. More overlapping feathers lie to either side of the strong-featured, standardized face. Large ear spools, the proper left one a replacement, flank the face. The rest of the figure is simply draped, with the hands resting on the knees. An overlarge strand of beads may not be original to the piece. A considerable amount of breakage, especially on the left half, has been reconsolidated with some areas of replacement.

Provenance
Skinner, Boston: sale 2209, 20 September 2003, Lot 49, p.17, ill. p.17

Estimate: $5,000-$7,000

47033

TEMPLE BRAZIER WITH A FACE
MASK OF A FERTILITY DEITY

Aztec
A.D. 1420–1520
Ceramic, stucco, and paint
Height 14⅜ in.

The overall brazier shape seen here was standardized by Aztec times, probably deriving from both Toltec and Mixtec prototypes. The body of this brazier is yellow ocher, with a pale green rope-like element forming the top rim and a two-inch band of pale green around the bottom. The deity in whose rites a brazier served was set on the front, with appropriate attributes added. Here a fertility deity face is shown with a greenish knotted necklace from which hang maize heads (based on their yellow coloring). The reddish face has three-lobed greenish elements issuing onto the cheeks from the lower edge of the nose, while the hair at top is pale green. Above the latter a yellow, braided headband is shown. Ear covers of yellowish green complete the facial area. To either side of the head pale green pleated paper fans (*amacalli*) are shown. These were a part of the headdresses of deity impersonators in danced rituals. The color throughout is age-dimmed, and there is overall surface abrasion. While the head remained intact, the brazier has been shattered and is reassembled with relatively few areas of replacement.

Provenance
William Siegal Gallery, Santa Fe, New Mexico

Estimate: $8,000-$12,000

47034

KNIFE WITH CARVED WOOD HANDLE

Aztec-Mixtec
A.D. 1300–1521
Wood and Chert, Weight 38 grams
Height 13 in. Width 1½ in.

The crisply carved wooden handle is connected to a broad chert blade of deep reddish brown color. The handle's primary image is a half figure whose open mouth suggests someone singing or chanting. An elaborate, frame-supported headdress backs this figure. It is possible that the entire unit represents an effigy such as would have been found in a shrine. Absolute iconographic identification is elusive, but the principal figure's facial expression and limply hanging hands make Xipe a likely identification. Xipe is an ancient deity, probably originating among early Gulf Coast agriculturalists. His primary meaning is as the flayed god of spring and regeneration. By Aztec-Mixtec times he was also patron of goldsmiths and jewelers. Here it is of note that the most likely identification of the headdress creature is Xiuhcoatl, the fire serpent. Robert Sonin, in a letter of 10 December 1982, cites a line from a hymn to Xipe that is of relevance: "The serpent of fire has set me free" (Laurette Séjourné. *Burning Water. Thought and Religion in Ancient Mexico.* New York and London: Thames & Hudson, 1956, p.151). The condition is very good. It is probable that the handle and blade, both ancient, have recently been put together.

The lot is sold with a statement of authenticity from the distinguished expert Robert Sonin.

Provenance
Leonard Patterson, New York
David Bernstein, New York

Estimate: $27,000-$30,000

A stone metalworking tool

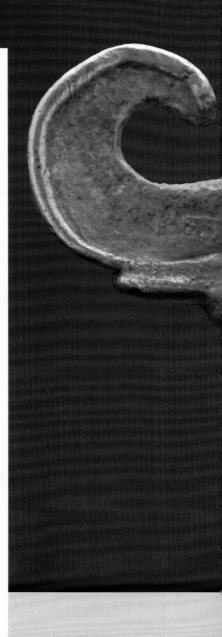

METALWORKING IN THE ANCIENT NEW WORLD

Our current knowledge indicates that skilled working with precious metals in the ancient New World began in what are today the Peruvian highlands and southern Ecuador and Colombia. Three metals form the core for the development of ritual, status, and practical uses of metals: copper, silver, and gold. In certain areas arsenic bronze and tin bronze were made and used, but not for any of the objects in the Hendershott Collection. It is important to keep in mind that none of the metal alloys developed were of a hardness and durability to serve as tools for use in stone cutting or carving.

The most noted early culture for which a moderate amount of artwork in precious metals survives is that of Chavín, centered in northern Peru, but influential elsewhere, especially along Peru's south coast. Surviving Chavín metalwork embodies the technique shared in other early metalwork from farther north in the modern nations of Ecuador and Colombia, that of hammering the metal into ever-thinner sheets through the alternating heating and cooling process known as annealing. Decoration was then achieved primarily using the repoussé technique, in which a moderately blunt scribing instrument is used to push design elements upward from the rear side of the sheet. This results in a relief image of varied levels of prominence. Some further detail might be added by chasing, which is using an often somewhat sharper tool to incise the metal from the upper side. These early pieces were made probably from about 900 to 800 B.C. onward, to use a conservative estimate.

Just when – and where – metal casting processes developed is more difficult to pinpoint. Since the earliest full exploitation of these processes occurred primarily in what are now parts of Ecuador and Colombia, we can assign these areas a central place. To this can be added the fact – at least from presently known material – that casting processes were seldom as central in Peru as further north. When, as with the Moche and later Chimú and Inca, casting was important, most surviving material is found in northern Peru. Cast pieces seem to have been made by 200 – 100 B.C., if not earlier.

Flourishing casting traditions developed during the earliest centuries of the present era. These were especially prolific in Colombia, from which they spread relatively quickly northward into the Central American isthmus. By A.D. 700 – 800 a number of traditions in modern Panama and Costa Rica were producing the kind of extraordinary cast pieces so well represented in the present collection.

The prevalent casting technique was the lost wax (*cire perdu*) method, in which a roughly shaped core, usually made of mixed clay and charcoal, serves as the matrix on which the artist modeled the final image in beeswax. It is possible that the latex-like sap of certain cactus may have been used as well. The completed, fully-detailed model was encased in clay. After this assemblage was dry, the caster prepared his metal for melting. The encased wax model was heated to the point that the clay fired and the wax melted (i.e., was "lost"). As soon as all of the wax had flowed out, the molten metal was poured into the resulting space. After cooling, the mold was broken to reveal the cast metal image. Any projecting hardened pouring channels (sprues) or other imperfections were abraded off as much as available tools allowed, and the piece was burnished (planished) and polished to finish it.

CENTRAL AMERICAN GOLD

Alimcingo · Cachan · Atoyac · Catahualtla · Compel · R. Vera Cruz

TLASCALLE

Subuila · Zacatula · Zumpango · Capotilan

Xiguacan · Guaxaca · Antequera · St. Martins Terre Haute

C. St. Peter · Catalula

B. St. Talt

ESPAGNE

GUAXACA

MER · Acapulco, ou Aquapulco · Inculula Malores

Pt. Marques

SOCONUSCO

CHIAPA

Pt. Escondido

R. Galei · Pt. Angels

DE · P. Guatulco · Salinas

Sosonusco

Lac Amuitan

R. Coatlan

SUD · R. Ayutla

R. Xicalapa · R. Michataya

Occident · d · 15 · e · 10 · f · 5

ampechy

S.Francois de Campechy

Cozumel

Lac de Bacalal

Boca Escondido

Par Royal

LUCATA

Bay Cheutumal

Patoia

St. Millan I.

Triest I.

R. Pet. et Paul

Abaco I.

Beef I.

Searles Clif

Laguna Termina

Quita Zuno

Salamanca

Guayana I.

I. de Leyn

Cap Camiron

I. dos Baixos

Chuckibul

Caratan

Golfe de Honduras

Guayona I.

Cap Honduras

Golf de Ilhot I.

Guanajos

Utila

Salmadina

I. Prnas

Meewe R.

R. Gamda

Meewen I.

P. del Negra

P. de Higueras

Puntas

Mahamena

Viciosa

Triumphe dela Cruz

R. Dulce

Amaligua

Porta Domos

Porta deSal

Monduaquo

G. Dolce

Truxillo

o Totasky

Cartago Bay

Coetroe

Bibara

B. Hondo

Pech

St. Georges

R.Guadago R.

la Bebra

C. Grat

Lago Cochanille

St. Pedro

Gratios o Dios

Valladolid o Comayagua

Comayagua ou St. Iago de Olancho

Paro R.

MOSQUITOS

R. Casmus

G. de Nic

MEXIQUE

HONDURAS

St. Salvador

la Trinidad

N. Segovia

Indian

R. Yara

Lempa

St. Michel

Amapal

AUDIENCE DE GUATIMALA

Villages

de Fonseca

Xeres

le Grand Vulcan de Munbacho

R. Varrejo

Traguz calpa

la Possession

Lac de Nicaragua

I. Parles

Realejo

Leon

Pipotero

Bla Ometepe

St. Bernardo St. Sebastian

I. de Manglar

R. Testa

Lipuapa

El pano

P. Solenti nam

Nicaragua ou Colorado R.

Granada

Monbache

Nicaragua

P. Cruys

Gr. atades Iuo Dedios

G. Papagajo

Paro

Restrella

Château de Austria

Bocca del Drago

P. S. Iuan

Cacao

Concepcion

P. de Velez

COSTA RICA

C. Blanco

Candishes Bay

Puebla

Golf de Salinas

I. Cano

Aranques

P. Lamons

VERA

Plt. di Burica

Ladrones

Conteras

Lucas ou 7 Isles

les Isles de Quicaro

Quicaro I.

Puercos

47035

PENDANT DEITY

Mixtec
A.D. 1000–1300
Gold, Weight 14 grams
Height 2¼ in. Width 1½ in.

The ancient ancestry of New World gold-working traditions is embodied in this piece. Its combination of a cast, sculptural upper portion with the flanged lower section flattened by hammering can be traced back through Costa Rican and Panamanian traditions to even earlier prototypes in Colombia. Another element that appears centuries earlier in Colombia is the so-called false-filigree, in which the thin string-like elements seen here in the headdress are modeled in wax and are integral with the cast rather being a filigree made from drawn wire.

As is often the case, exact identification of Late Classic Central Mexican deities is elusive. Here, the headdress does not provide information in spite of its elegance and technical prowess. The deity is shown as a half-figure with hands on the abdomen and a single-strand bead necklace centered with a celt-shaped pendant. Claw-like ear pendants are visible between face and headdress. The powerful Roman-nosed face compels attention. The softening surface wear on the hands indicates considerable ancient use of the pendant. On the hammer-finished flanges, the proper left has a large, anciently-added patch. A cracked separation at the neck has been repaired, but the condition is still fragile.

Provenance
David Bernstein, New York

Estimate: $12,000-$15,000

47036

CIRCULAR BREAST PLATE

Costa Rica or Panama
A.D. 700–1500
Gold, Weight 72.6 grams
Diameter 6½ in.

Made from a fairly heavy gold sheet, this circular breastplate is edged by two rows of fine-scaled repoussé beading along the edge. Inside this, a circle of much larger bosses completes the décor. Two holes for suspension are punched in the upper center. The condition is moderately good, with several minor cracks or tears, some wrinkling, and age stains.

This lot is sold with a statement of authenticity from the distinguished expert Robert Sonin.

Provenance
Charles Craig, Santa Barbara

Estimate: $2,500-$4,000

47037

CIRCULAR BREASTPLATE

Costa Rica or Panama
A.D. 700–1500
Gold, Weight 18.9 grams
Diameter 5⅜ in.

The rather broad repoussé bordering band on this gold breastplate is edged on outside and inside by fine, lightly punched dots. There is a diagonal tear from the edge through the border between the suspension holes, along with surface crinkling overall. There is a reddish age patination.

The lot is sold with a statement of authenticity from the distinguished expert Robert Sonin.

Provenance
Charles Craig, Santa Barbara

Estimate: $800-$1,200

47038

CIRCULAR BREASTPLATE

Costa Rica or Panama
A.D. 700–1500
Gold, Weight 44.3 grams
Diameter 6 in.

A rather broad flat repoussé band borders this gold breastplate. Two widely-spaced suspension holes are outlined by a raised half-circle which terminates at the bordering band. In fair condition, the plate was folded in ancient times, leaving crease marks and minor cracks.

The lot is sold with a statement of authenticity from the distinguished expert Robert Sonin.

Provenance
Charles Craig, Santa Barbara

Estimate: $1,000-$1,500

47039

CIRCULAR BREASTPLATE

Costa Rica or Panama
A.D. 700–1500
Gold, Weight 21.2 grams
Diameter 5¼ in.

A broad band defining the edge of the gold breastplate is outlined on either side with closely spaced shallow punches. The suspension holes are widely spaced. The condition is moderately good, with age patination and some surface crinkling.

The lot is sold with a statement of authenticity from the distinguished expert Robert Sonin.

Provenance
Charles Craig, Santa Barbara

Estimate: $800-$1,200

47040

CIRCULAR BREASTPLATE

Costa Rica or Panama
A.D. 700–1500
Gold, Weight 59.2 grams
Diameter 6¾ in.

The relatively thin solid breastplate is bordered by a carefully chased pattern of two continuous, interwoven bands. Two small suspension holes were punched far apart just inside this band. A four-inch long tear crosses below these holes, and one fold crease is clearly visible at the viewer's lower left. There are several minor tears at the edges.

The lot is sold with a statement of authenticity from the distinguished expert Robert Sonin.

Provenance
Charles Craig, Santa Barbara

Estimate: $1,500-$2,500

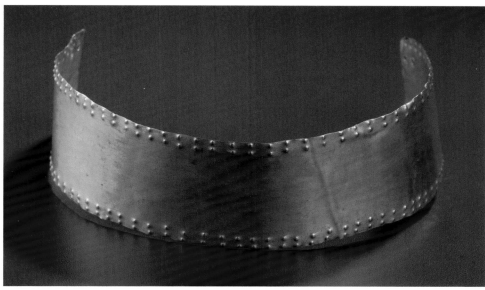

47041

ARMBAND OR CUFF

Costa Rica or Panama
A.D. 700–1500
Gold, Weight 54.3 grams
Length 13 in. Width 1¾ in.

This medium-heavy gold cuff is bordered at top and bottom by two rows of small repoussé beading. Careful spacing to create vertically-oriented pairs establishes a rhythmically pleasing effect. Arm cuffs are rarely encountered. The condition is good, with one fold crease. There are four tie-holes at each end.

The lot is sold with a statement of authenticity from the distinguished expert Robert Sonin.

Provenance
Charles Craig, Santa Barbara

Estimate: $2,500-$3,000

47042

BEADS

Costa Rica or Panama
A.D. 700–1500
Gold, Weight 18.2 grams
Round Beads Diameter ⅛ in. – ¼ in.
Tubular Beads Diameter ¼ in. – ⅞ in.

The consistent diameter size suggests that these beads may all have been used together originally. They have been restrung alternating three round beads with one longer tubular bead. The condition is fair, with some beads cracked or bent.

The lot is sold with a statement of authenticity from the distinguished expert Robert Sonin.

Provenance
Charles Craig, Santa Barbara

Estimate: $1,200-$1,500

47043

THREE BELLS

Costa Rica or Panama
A.D. 700–1500
Gold, Weight 41.3 grams
Length 1⅛ in. (2 largest bells)

Gold bells with integrally cast suspension loops were a favored component of dress—and at times of ritual—from Colombia northward through lower Central America. These examples in good quality gold are in good condition.

The lot is sold with a statement of authenticity from the distinguished expert Robert Sonin.

Provenance
Charles Craig, Santa Barbara

Estimate: $900-$1,200

47044

CELT

Panama or Costa Rica
A.D. 700–1500
Gold, Weight 384.3 grams
Length 4⅛ in. Width 1¾ in.

With a weight of 384.2 grams, this very rare cast gold celt is truly massive. Its purpose may well have been ceremonial, especially given the amount of gold used. "It was cast in an open mold with an upward slope at one end to pre-form and taper the sharp edge" (Robert Sonin, letter of 1 June 2005). Other than a few small stains and scratches, the condition is very good.

The lot is sold with a statement of authenticity from the distinguished expert Robert Sonin.

Provenance
Charles Craig, Santa Barbara

Estimate: $7,000-$10,000

47045

EAR ORNAMENTS

Costa Rica or Panama
A.D. 700–1500
Copper, Weight 110 grams
Height 3½ in. Width 1⅞ in.

This pair of unusually large copper ear ornaments
is structured so that the elongated shafts rather than
the outer end bear the ornament. These shafts are
done as stacked rows of an identical open work design
of paired spirals in continuous rows around the
circumference. There are some minor losses, as well as
minor surface corrosion.

The lot is sold with a statement of authenticity from
the distinguished expert Robert Sonin.

Provenance
Charles Craig, Santa Barbara

Estimate: $4,000-$6,000

47046

SHAMAN WITH ARMS RAISED

Veraguas, Chiriquí, Diquís
A.D. 700–1500
Gold, Weight 30.1 grams
Height 3 in. Width 1½ in.

This stiffly posed shaman with raised arms shows stylistic
descent from the Colombian gold working tradition,
primarily that of the Quimbaya area. The treatment at the ear
area suggests either parts of the headdress or an elaborate hair
arrangement. Overall the casting shows a number of flaws, but
the condition is good.

The lot is sold with a statement of authenticity from the
distinguished expert Robert Sonin.

Provenance
Charles Craig, Santa Barbara

Estimate: $1,500-$3,000

47047

PENDANT: STANDING SHAMAN FIGURE

Costa Rica or Panama
A.D. 700–1500
Tumbaga, Weight 7.8 grams
Height 2¼ in. Width 1¼ in.

The frontal male shaman stands with legs and arms akimbo, the hands grasping tubular objects which attach to the thighs. A headdress of overlapping paired upward-thrusting bars in V-pattern is above a crudely conventionalized face with double loops at its sides. Condition is poor, with surface corrosion and losses.

The lot is sold with a statement of authenticity from the distinguished expert Robert Sonin.

Provenance
Charles Craig, Santa Barbara

Estimate: $800-$1,200

47048

PENDANT: STANDING MALE FIGURE

Costa Rica or Panama
A.D. 700–1500
Gold, Weight 37.5 grams
Height 2⅛ in. Width 1½ in.

This broad-faced naked male stands spread-legged on large feet. He holds gourd rattles in each hand. From a braided headband a short central cylinder rises from the head. The condition is very good.

The lot is sold with a statement of authenticity from the distinguished expert Robert Sonin.

Provenance
Charles Craig, Santa Barbara

Estimate: $2,000-$3,000

47049

SHAMAN WITH FLEXED LEGS

Costa Rica or Panama
A.D. 700–1500
Tumbaga, Weight 25.5 grams
Height 3 in. Width 1½ in.

The legs of this badly corroded figure are so strongly flexed that it appears more seated than not. A rather naturalistic face is surmounted by a damaged, once-elaborate headdress. The condition is poor, with both lower arms and portions of the headdress missing, along with severe corrosion.

The lot is sold with a statement of authenticity from the distinguished expert Robert Sonin.

Provenance
Charles Craig, Santa Barbara

Estimate: $500-$800

47050

FRONTAL SHAMAN FIGURE

Costa Rica or Panama
A.D. 700–1500
Copper, Weight 9.4 grams
Height 2⅜ in. Width 1 in.

This smiling frontal male stands with arms bent at the elbows to show the palms of the upraised hands with fingers curled forward. His multi-toed feet point downward. A headdress formed by a central trapezoid above a band and flanked by double-band streamers curving down to the shoulders above flap-like ears completes the image. Condition is fair with considerable surface corrosion.

This lot is sold with a statement of authenticity from the distinguished expert Robert Sonin.

Provenance
Charles Craig, Santa Barbara

Estimate: $500-$800

47051

PENDANT: THREE-FIGURE SHAMANIC GROUP

Costa Rica or Panama
A.D. 700–1500
Gold, Weight 115.1 grams
Height 3¼ in. Width 3¼ in.

This pendant remains from what must originally have represented a notable moment of ritual shamanic activity. A larger central corpulent figure plays a horizontal drum, flanked by two smaller flute-playing animal–human crosses. The drummer's body has carefully-worked undulating snakelike forms moving along either side of what remains of the body. The condition is very poor.

The lot is sold with a statement of authenticity from the distinguished expert Robert Sonin.

Provenance
Charles Craig, Santa Barbara

Estimate: $1,800-$2,400

47052

PENDANT: SHAMANIC FIGURE

Costa Rica or Panama
A.D. 700–1500
Gold, Weight 82.1 grams
Height 4¼ in. Width 2⅞ in.

This hieratically-designed pendant portrays a complex shaman standing on what was once a bar featuring outward facing mythologized zoomorphs at either side of his feet (the bar's right half and most of the figure's right leg are now missing). The piece is terminated at top by a mirror image of the basal bar. The principal figure's head is tapir-derived, but given sharply-pointed teeth. He holds in his mouth a braided double-headed serpent whose heads rest at the breast area of the figure. The otherwise naked shaman grasps a further serpent in each hand, their heads facing upward. Other than the mentioned missing parts, the condition is good.

The lot is sold with a statement of authenticity from the distinguished expert Robert Sonin.

Provenance
Charles Craig, Santa Barbara

Estimate: $2,500-$3,500

47053

PENDANT: FIGURE HOLDING A GROUP OF BIRDS

Costa Rica or Panama
A.D. 700–1500
Gold, Weight 33.8 grams
Height 1⅞ in. Width 2 in.

The broad, flattened face of this pendant illustrates a close relationship to Colombian styles. Other unusual characteristics are the abbreviated body, the string arms, and the Pinocchio-like extension of the nose to act as a support for the group of birds which is being "presented." Each bird head is fully defined, though one is now missing and others somewhat damaged, while the winged bodies are defined as zigzag lines along a flattened shared surface. There are losses at the edges and the upper headdress area is now missing.

The lot is sold with a statement of authenticity from the distinguished expert Robert Sonin.

Provenance
Charles Craig, Santa Barbara

Estimate: $1,800-$2,400

47054

PENDANT: PAIR OF BATS

Veraguas, Chiriquí, Diquís
A.D. 700–1500
Tumbaga, Weight 29.2 grams
Height 1⅜ in. Width 1⅞ in.

These joined bats are seen as though from below, with all four paws visible and pointed side tabs resembling short extended wings. Each has two outward-curled tails. Raised circular wells on the stomachs were intended to have inlays, and forward-projecting hooks—the proper right now missing—held dangling gold disks, though only the center one remains. There is the overall surface corrosion characteristic of *tumbaga.*

Provenance
Charles Craig, Santa Barbara

Estimate: $900-$1,200

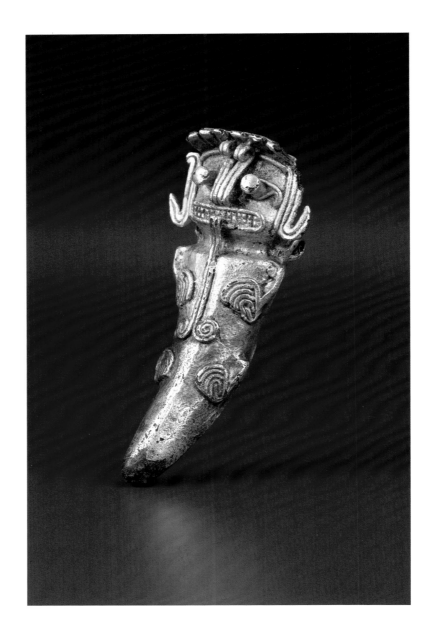

47055

TOOTH-SHAPED PENDANT

Panama
A.D. 700–1500
Tumbaga, Weight 39.7 grams
Height 3⅛ in. Width 1½ in.

This tooth-shaped pendant depicts a grotesque mythic being whose claw-like hands and feet
are portrayed against the body in a manner reminiscent stylistically of Coclé painted ceramics.
This fits with the shape and details of the head and the extended bifurcated tongue, these being
characteristics of actual tusk pendants excavated at Coclé. The condition is good, with a corrosion
loss at the proper upper left of the head and black-stained tip.

The lot is sold with a statement of authenticity from the distinguished expert Robert Sonin.

Provenance
Charles Craig, Santa Barbara

Estimate: $4,000-$6,000

47056

PENDANT, FOUR ANIMALS IN A ROW

Veraguas, Chiriquí, Diquís
A.D. 200–700
Tumbaga, Weight 30.7 grams
Height 1⅛ in. Width 2 in.

Such groups of animals with tails curled over the backs are found from the Colombian Caribbean area up through Central America, further confirming that image configurations traveled along with technical knowledge. The proper right animal is missing its right front leg and the attached upper supporting bar and suspension loop. A casting break is in the upper bar in front of the proper left animal. There is some overall corrosion.

Provenance
Charles Craig, Santa Barbara

Estimate: $1,200-$1,500

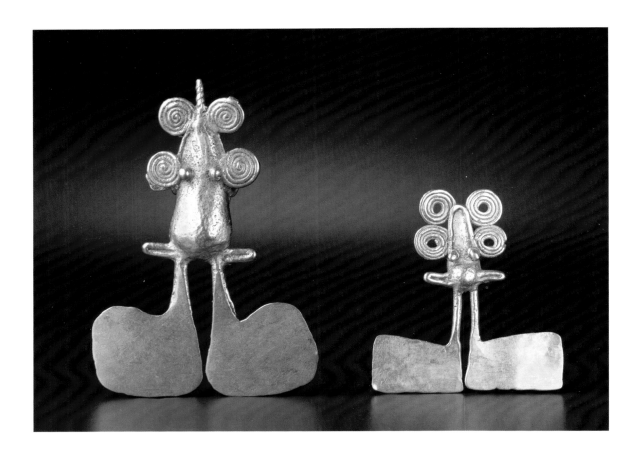

47057

ZOOMORPHIC PENDANTS

Veraguas, Chiriquí, Diquís
A.D. 700–1500
Gold, (A) Weight 35.8 grams (B) Weight 14 grams
(A) Length 3⅛ in. Width 2⅛ in.
(B) Length 2⅛ in. Width 1¾ in.

Two interpretations are suggested by the creatures represented, one land-based, the other a denizen of the sea. The pointed-nosed piece could be a shrew, though this is less likely with the other. Both might be seen as squid, which are represented on pottery from the region. The condition is good.

Provenance
Charles Craig, Santa Barbara

Estimate: $3,000-$4,000

47058

FROG-FORM PENDANT

Costa Rica or Panama
A.D. 700–1500
Tumbaga, Weight 10.1 grams
Length 1½ in. Width 1⅛ in.

In addition to its large eyes formed by cup-shapes, this frog has a third, larger cup-shape at the lower back. All three would originally have held a stone setting. The flanged feet are made of many thin parallel lines, while angular shapes to either side of the nose may have served as front legs. A bifurcated curl issues from the mouth. The condition is fair, with some surface corrosion and loss.

The lot is sold with a statement of authenticity from the distinguished expert Robert Sonin.

Provenance
Charles Craig, Santa Barbara

Estimate: $200-$300

47059

FROG-FORM PENDANT

Veraguas, Chiriquí, Diquís
A.D. 700–1500
Tumbaga, Weight 13.1 grams
Height 1¾ in. Width 1¼ in.

The large-eyed frog has a central band running from the nose to the end of the back, this formed by framing plain strips enclosing a double gridded band. Suspension loops are at the front feet. In addition to overall light corrosion the tip of the proper left rear foot is missing.

Provenance
Charles Craig, Santa Barbara

Estimate: $500-$700

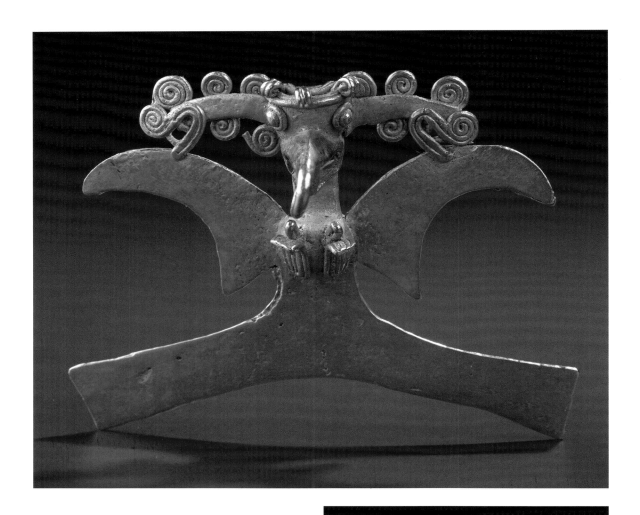

47060

BIRD-FORM PENDANT

Costa Rica or Panama
A.D. 700–1500
Gold, Weight 73.2 grams
Height 2⅜ in. Width 3¼ in.

The unusually horizontal presentation of this bird-
form pendent, especially the tail, gives this pendant
an athletic quality. The wiry liveliness is reinforced by
the thin beak and the attached circular loop intended
for a dangler. The simplified zoomorphic creatures
extending to either side of the head are also elongated.
Condition is good except for a missing spiral at the
proper right beak base, and a slight separation where
the proper right flanking creature is joined to the bird's
head.

The lot is sold with a statement of authenticity from the
distinguished expert Robert Sonin.

Provenance
Charles Craig, Santa Barbara

Estimate: $7,000-$10,000

47061

BIRD-FORM PENDANT

Costa Rica or Panama
A.D. 700–1500
Copper, Weight 21 grams
Height 2½ in. Width 2⅞ in.

Head decorating elements and wings of this unusual bird-form pendant are in elegant rhythmic harmony. Their delicacy coincides with the feel of the rest of the execution. The feet and legs are unusually prominent. The lower proper right tail is partly missing, and there is some surface corrosion due to its high copper content. Otherwise, condition is fair.

The lot is sold with a statement of authenticity from the distinguished expert Robert Sonin.

Provenance
Charles Craig, Santa Barbara

Estimate: $800-$1,200

47062

BIRD-FORM PENDANT

A.D. 700–1500
Costa Rica or Panama
Gold
Height 4¾ in. Width 3⅝ in.

The primary interest of this rather large bird-form pendant lies in its showing the result of the ritual "killing" that was a prevalent ancient American ceremonial practice. This was done for several related reasons: to neutralize an object's inherent power; to free its spirit before burial; and to deflect potential negative energies from previous owners, especially at times when rulership structures were changed. Here the results of pounding with a heavy stone are especially visible in the bent and cracked beak and the virtually obliterated feet. The proper left wing was folded at its juncture point, and the other wing is heavily hammered.

The lot is sold with a statement of authenticity from the distinguished expert Robert Sonin.

Provenance
Charles Craig, Santa Barbara

Estimate: $800-$1,200

47063

BIRD-FORM PENDANT

Panama or Costa Rica
A.D. 700–1500
Tumbaga, Weight 65.4 grams
Height 3 in. Width 4¼ in.

Following in its overall design the standard "displayed" convention, this bird-form pendant has several distinctive elements as well. The infrequently-seen knobbed caruncle on its beak probably indicates that it is a vulture. Also distinctive are the inclusion of the opposed rear talon and the unusually prominent eyes. A low relief braid bordered by bands is along the lower edge of each wing. The back shows several changes or corrections to the wax original made during the modeling process. Where the surface-gilding remains, it is unusually bright. In addition to loss at the outer upper edge of the proper left wing, there are both black corrosion areas and green oxidation deposits.

Provenance
Charles Craig, Santa Barbara

Estimate: $1,500-$2,500

47064

BIRD-FORM PENDANT

Costa Rica or Panama
A.D. 700–1500
Gold, Weight 45.1 grams
Height 2½ in. Width 2½ in.

This lively pendant in heavy gold has a very unusual wing treatment. The angled wings resemble human arms, with their lower edge rimmed by spaced curls. These arm-wings terminate in upside-down beaked birds' heads where hands might be. The head is squarely formed, with bulging eyes far to the side. Paired curls lie at either side of the flattened head top. Loop ear ornaments complete the image. The condition is good.

The lot is sold with a statement of authenticity from the distinguished expert Robert Sonin.

Provenance
Charles Craig, Santa Barbara

Estimate: $6,000-$9,000

47065

BIRD-FORM PENDANT

Costa Rica or Panama
A.D. 700–1500
Gold, Weight 36.2 grams
Height 2⅝ in. Width 2¾ in.

Heavy gold was used in making this large-beaked, triple-crested raptor. The talons are raised and tensed as though ready to capture prey. From the back an interesting series of ancient maker's additions, patches, and repairs is visible, especially on the wings. Condition is good except for the loss of a double band along the proper right side of the head.

The lot is sold with a statement of authenticity from the distinguished expert Robert Sonin.

Provenance
Charles Craig, Santa Barbara

Estimate: $4,000-$6,000

47066

PENDANT: SUPERNATURAL SHAMAN HOLDING CLUBS

Coclé (or Coclé-derived)
A.D. 650–1520
Gold, Weight 42.25 grams
Height 2½ in. Width 3⅛ in.

The supernatural shaman depicted by this pendant is most like an insect with its body which tapers to a point and the antenna-like projections at the sides of the head. The rather flat, squarish face has a small upturned curl at the lower tip of a vertical strip which divides the face, which furthers the insect-like appearance. The heraldically frontal being holds unusual, large clubs which flange horizontally far out to either side. Lower feet at either side of the abdomen hold flattened plant-like elements. The cordlike arms relate to works from the Coclé style region. The condition is good.

The lot is sold with a statement of authenticity from the distinguished expert Robert Sonin.

Provenance
Charles Craig, Santa Barbara

Estimate: $4,000-$5,000

47067

FOUR FROG-FORM PENDANTS

Costa Rica or Panama
A.D. 700/800–1500
Tumbaga
(A) Height 2 in.   Width 2¼ in.   Weight 25.1 grams
(B) Height 2¼ in.   Width 1½ in.   Weight 26.0 grams
(C) Height 1⅜ in.   Width ¾ in.   Weight 4.1 grams
(D) Height 1 in.   Width 1⅜ in.   Weight 5.9 grams

This lot is comprised of four *tumbaga* frog-form pendants. As pictured, the upper left (A) is of a fat figured frog with large paddle-form rear legs. The upper right frog (B) has bulging rattle eyes and four water or breath spirals emanating from the mouth. The lower right frog (C) has a slim body, beady eyes, breath/water spirals at the mouth, paddle rear feet, and a framed strip of spirals running down the back. The last pendant is pictured on the lower left (D). It is a double frog, each with beady eyes and a segmented strip running from the nose down the back. This pendant has suffered losses on several limbs. The condition of each pendant varies, with some surface losses on all.

Provenance
Charles Craig, Santa Barbara

Estimate: $600-$900

47068

FROG-FORM PENDANT

Costa Rica or Panama
A.D. 700–1500
Gold, Weight 10.1 grams
Height 1½ in. Width ¾ in.

This tiny cast frog has four breath or water spirals emanating from the mouth area. The pointed face is outlined with a narrow band ending around goggle eyes. The paddle feet and the rear end are poorly cast, leaving spaces and a rough finish.

Provenance
Charles Craig, Santa Barbara

Estimate: $400-$600

47069

BIRD FIGURE, RITUALLY KILLED

Costa Rica or Panama
A.D. 700–1500
Gold (low grade), Weight 46.4 grams
Height 3¾ in. Width 1 in.

Ancient items were often "killed" or mangled to contain or control their power when ritual use was completed. This bird figure appears to have suffered this fate with a severe mid-section break from folding as well as other damage. This left it in poor condition, with surface corrosion and a modern patch of solder at mid-point as a repair attempt. Double spiral forms perch on the beak and flank the tail point. A braided cord delineates the neck.

Provenance
Charles Craig, Santa Barbara

Estimate: $600-$800

47070

THREE C-SHAPED RINGS

Costa Rica or Panama
A.D. 700–1500
Gold, Weight 43.1 grams
(A) Height 1³⁄₁₆ in.   Width 1½ in.
(B) Height 1¹⁄₁₆ in.   Width 1⁵⁄₁₆ in.
(C) Height ¹⁵⁄₁₆ in.   Width 1⅛ in.

Gold rings such as these are described in many
publications as nose rings in spite of their
considerable weight and uncomfortably rough ends.
Perhaps they could have been used as monetary trade
goods. Their general condition is fair.

Provenance
Charles Craig, Santa Barbara

Estimate: $300-$400

47071

BAND-FORM CROWN

Costa Rica or Panama
A.D. 700–1500
Gold, Weight 12.0 grams
Length 21³⁄₈ in. Width 1½ in.

This crown has a double row of repoussé beading bordering top and bottom edges. Four puncture holes at each end
were probably used to tie the crown into a circle when worn. There is slight puckering on the ends and some folds in
the body, otherwise the condition is good.

Provenance
Charles Craig, Santa Barbara

Estimate: $1,500-$2,500

47072

FROG PENDANT WITH DOUBLE-HEADED SERPENT

Costa Rica or Panama
A.D. 700–1500
Gold, Weight 32.4 grams
Height 2 in. Width 1¾ in.

This fat bodied frog pendant has bead eyes set into rings. Paddle feet, which are striated by horizontal and diagonal lines, suggest rear legs. A double-headed snake emanates from the frog's mouth. The snake is lined along the length of the body. Two water spirals are attached at the front curves of the snake. The snake heads are banded triangle shapes with eyes that repeat those of the frog. The condition is good, with a slight casting fault toward the rear proper right side of the body.

Provenance
Charles Craig, Santa Barbara

Estimate: $2,000-$3,000

47073

FROG PENDANT WITH SPIRAL ON HEAD

Chiriquí or Diquís
A.D. 700–1550
Gold, Weight 47.8 grams
Height 2⅝ in. Width 2¾ in.

This cast gold frog has three spirals emanating from the two corners and the front of its mouth. A double spiral forms an S-shape on the crest of its head. These elements represent either breath (life) or water (fertility). Rattles serve as eyes on either side of the head. The rear legs end in typical large flat paddles. Suspension loops for wearing terminate the ends of the front legs.

Provenance
Charles Craig, Santa Barbara

Estimate: $3,000-$4,000

47074

DOUBLE FROG PENDANT

Veraguas, Chiriquí
A.D. 700–1500
Gold, Weight 60.5 grams
Height 2½ in. Width 3⅝ in.

These conjoined cast gold frogs share a center rear paddle-shaped foot and an ear whorl. Double breath spirals emanate from each frog's nose. These spirals may also have been symbolic of the water in which the eggs of the frog are fertilized. The four prominent bulging eyes also serve as rattles. Suspension loops are created at the ends of the four front legs. Large paddle-like feet form the ends of the frogs' rear outside legs.

Provenance
Charles Craig, Santa Barbara

Estimate: $4,000-$6,000

47075

FANTASY ANIMAL PAIR ON BAR

Veraguas, Chiriquí, or Diquís
A.D. 200 – 700
Gold, Weight 53.1 grams
Height 2¼ in. Width 1½ in.

Two like mammals side by side clasp a bar with their front paws. Three small versions of the same mammal are seated on the tops of the front paws of the main pair. The snouts are long and pointed, and thick tails drag behind. These are possibly representations of a coati or a lizard. The four eyes are also rattles, and the heads are crested with three knobs. The piece could be worn as a pendant, using the three suspension loops formed by the front paws grasping the bar.

Provenance
Charles Craig, Santa Barbara

Estimate: $3,000-$4,000

47076

BIRD-FORM PENDANT

Costa Rica or Panama
A.D. 700–1500
Gold, Weight 14.8 grams
Height 2⅜ in. Width 2⅛ in.

This bird-form pendant has a curved beak and forward-thrusting talons. The flat, flanged tail has recently been re-welded to the main body. There are some casting pits on the extended wing flanges. Bead eyes give the bird a vigilant gaze. The head projections, perhaps representing feather tufts, are damaged, with pieces missing.

Provenance
Charles Craig, Santa Barbara

Estimate: $2,000-$2,500

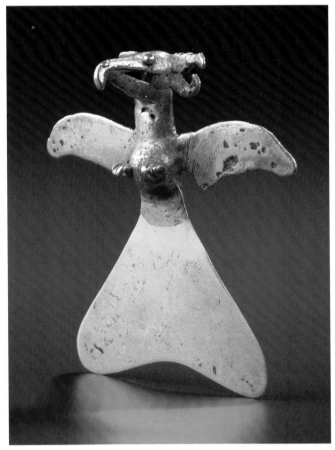

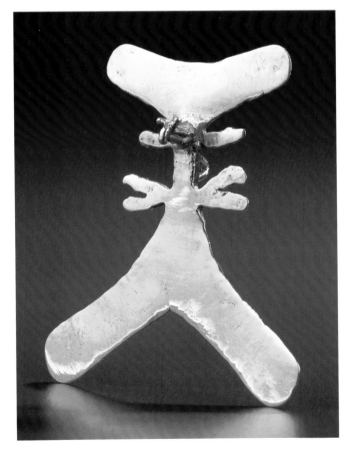

47077

BIRD-FORM PENDANT

Costa Rica or Panama
A.D. 700–1500
Gold, Weight 13 grams
Height 2¼ in. Width 2 in.

This flat bird pendant has a small forward-projecting beak that hooks down at the tip. There are two vertical projections from the beak tip as well. Flat flanges project from the top of the head, from the ear area, as wings, and as a bifurcated tail. There is a suspension loop at the rear of the neck. The condition is good.

Provenance
Charles Craig, Santa Barbara

Estimate: $2,000-$2,500

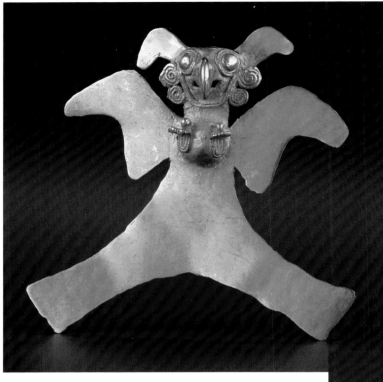

47078

AVIAN PENDANT WITH WING-STYLE EARS

Diquís
A.D. 700–1520
Gold, Weight 69.1 grams
Height 3⅞ in. Width 3⅞ in.

This bird-formed pendant embodies several characteristics of the Jalaca type, including double ear whorls and chin bands under a prominent hooked beak. Bulging circular eyes are also banded for emphasis. The bird represented may be a harpy eagle. Flat flanges represent the wings, exaggerated bifurcated tail, and head tufts. The talons jut out from the chest ready to carry off its prey. At contact period indigenous people of the area believed that harpy eagles carried the souls of the dead to the nether world.

Provenance
Charles Craig, Santa Barbara

Estimate: $6,000-$8,000

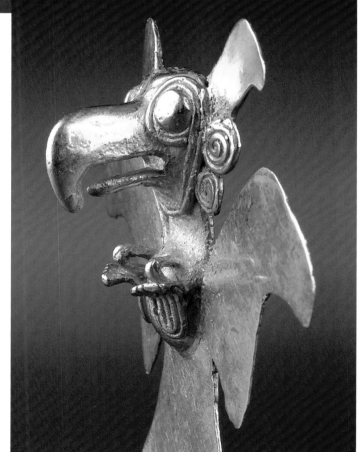

47079

BIRD-FORM PENDANT

Diquís
A.D. 500–1550
Gold, Weight 178.2 grams
Height 6 in. Width 5¼ in.

This bird pendant in the form of a harpy eagle has a prominent hooked beak that juts forward over a triangular breast area. Grasping claws are ready imminently to seize prey. Stylized crocodile heads protrude from each side of the bird's head, and simply rendered bird heads are attached at each cheek area. The bead-like eyes are set into rings, and curled projections top the head. Seen from above, the head is covered by integrally cast criss-cross openwork strips. The flattened stylized plaque represents extended wings and bifurcated tail feathers. A suspension loop is on the back neck area. Major casting faults crease and crack the body area, and numerous remaining hammer marks suggest that the planishing was never completed.

Provenance
Charles Craig, Santa Barbara

Estimate: $10,000-$15,000

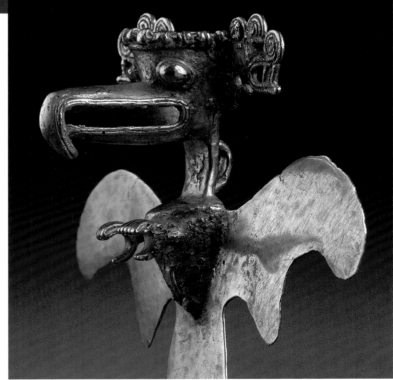

47080

FIGURE BITING DOUBLE-HEADED SNAKE-BODIED CREATURE

Coclé Province or Azuero Peninsula
A.D. 650–1520
Gold, Weight 133.2 grams
Height 4¼ in. Width 2¾ in.

This figure was worn as a pendant suspended from the two loops at the back flanking the neck. With knees slightly bent, arms bent at the elbows, and hands clenched, the figure bites the ribbon-like body of a double-headed monster. The monster's heads are crested crocodiles with up-turned muzzles and serrated teeth in gaping jaws. Triangular shapes representing crocodile scutes outline the heads and front legs of the monsters. These triangular shapes and snout curls are repeated as an elongated headdress for the figure and also as projections from his waist along his legs to his feet, in all cases further enforcing the crocodilian presence. The figure wears a short kilt and a collar that suggests beading. There are nine concave cup-shaped forms on the body, including one representing the nose, that were probably inlaid with colored stones to further enhance the power of this piece. The condition is very good.

Provenance
Charles Craig, Santa Barbara

Estimate: $18,000-$24,000

47081

PENDANT: STANDING MONSTROUS FIGURES WITH PADDLES

Coclé Province or Azuero Peninsula
A.D. 650–1520
Gold, Weight 122 grams
Height 2⁷⁄₁₆ in. Width 4¹³⁄₁₆ in.

Two frontal male human-bodied figures with crested crocodile heads stand side-by-side on a round bar which ends in knobs. Their heads turned outward, the figures hold large trapezoidal paddles in their outer hands, while their inner hands, fingers touching, grasp an inverted U-shaped twisted cord. A large double crest joins the two heads and forms a visual balance with the bottom bar. The double-bar handles of the paddles end at bottom in outward curves and each has two scutes on the outer edge; the effect is that of an abbreviated downward-facing profile crested crocodile head. The naked figures have double bands at waist and ankles and a triple band across the upper chest. The heads and the hands are fully three-dimensional in their development, so that they are as complete when seen from the back as from the front. The condition is excellent.

Provenance
Charles Craig, Santa Barbara

Estimate: $12,000-$15,000

47082

MAN WITH RATTLES AND SERRATED HEADDRESS

Chiriquí
A.D. 1000–1550
Gold, Weight 61.1 grams
Height 2¾ in. Width 2⅝ in.

This frontal male figure stands with knees bent, grasping rounded gourd rattles in each hand. He wears a necklace with one round bead drop. On his head is a complex headdress of two open squares with a top serrated edge possibly depicting feathers. A band starting and ending with a circular plug stretches from jaw to temple and across the forehead, framing the face. Double whorls, possibly ear ornaments, almost fill the inner space of the N form on either side of the head. His coffee-bean eyes, closed lips, and prominent nose give the figure a trance-like appearance. The bent knees and elbows suggest a ritual dance.

Provenance
Charles Craig, Santa Barbara

Estimate: $5,000-$7,000

47083

CRAB PENDANT

Diquís
A.D. 700–1550
Gold, Weight 71.2 grams
Height 2½ in. Width 2⅛ in.

This realistic and appealing three-dimensional crab pendant was cast using the lost wax technique. The suspension loop is on the back top, allowing the crab to be worn with pincers up. The bulging bullet eyes set into rings are characteristic of the style of this area. A pellet contained in the body rattles when the pendant is moved. The condition is good.

Provenance
Charles Craig, Santa Barbara

Estimate: $4,000-$6,000

47084

SUPERNATURAL SHARK PENDANT

Veraguas, Chiriquí, Diquís
A.D. 700−1500
Gold, Weight 134.6 grams
Length 5 1/16 in. Width 3 1/8 in.

Its primary shark identity marked by two prominent dorsal fins, the supernatural nature of this creature is emphasized by the S-shaped serpent-headed barbles. Spiralled bubbles move along these, with two larger bubbles at the corners of the shark's mouth overlying the barbles. Paired side fins and a flattened conceptualized tail of double-U form complete the main features. Visible only when the pendant is turned over is the shark's gaping mouth with strong triangular teeth. Robert Sonin makes a particularly interesting technical comment: "The fins and tails were all hammered to get the final shapes and hammer planished to get a smooth surface on top and a textured surface underneath—the work of a fine craftsman." Condition is excellent.

The lot is sold with a statement of authenticity from the distinguished expert Robert Sonin.

Provenance
Charles Craig, Santa Barbara

Estimate: $16,000-$20,000

47085

PENDANT FROG

Veraguas, Chiriquí
A.D. 700–1500
Gold, Weight 63.1 grams
Length 3 in. Width 3⅛ in.

Four large, coiled bubble forms line the frog's mouth, while an openwork band of similar coils moves from the nose across the head and down the back. The rear foot areas have been flattened by hammering into broad flanges to give stability when the pendant was worn. Minute edge-cracks on these demonstrate the limit beyond which hammering could not continue. The front feet have been looped to form a means for suspension. The condition is good.

The lot is sold with a statement of authenticity from the distinguished expert Robert Sonin.

Provenance
Charles Craig, Santa Barbara

Estimate: $5,000-$7,000

47086

DOUBLE FROG PENDANT

Veraguas, Chiriquí, Diquís
A.D. 700–1500
Gold, Weight 123.76 grams
Height 4⅝ in. Width 2¹¹⁄₁₆ in.

This massive pendant shows two frog supernaturals joined at mid-body as though moving in opposite directions from a central energy source. The integrally-cast suspension loops indicate a vertical orientation when worn. The bulging-eyed heads have unusual three-ribboned nostril emanations and large S-shaped streams emerge in opposing directions from their mouths. These are punctuated by coiled "bubbles" and end in serpent heads. The front feet are flipper-like and are shown in the action of propelling the creatures apart, imparting unusual dynamism. Casting gate stubs are visible at the mouths of the two lower serpents. Condition is excellent.

The lot is sold with a statement of authenticity from the distinguished expert Robert Sonin.

Provenance
Charles Craig, Santa Barbara

Estimate: $18,000-$24,000

47087

FROG FORM PENDANT

Diquís, Veraguas, Chiriquí
A.D. 700–1500
Gold, Weight 65.91 grams
Height 3⁷⁄₁₆ in. Width 3¹³⁄₁₆ in.

The large eyes are a notable feature of this frog, their bell-shape announcing the fact that they contain pellets and jingle faintly with motion. Three pairs of curls issue from the mouth, and two banded loops indicate nostril emanations. A gridded band divides the body, whose front feet were made as loops for suspension, while the rear feet were hammered into broad spatulate forms to stabilize the rather heavy upper body when worn. The present condition is good.

The lot is sold with a statement of authenticity from the distinguished expert Robert Sonin.

Provenance
Charles Craig, Santa Barbara

Estimate: $6,000-$9,000

47088

TURTLE-FORM BELL PENDANT

Veraguas–Chiriquí
A.D. 700–1500
Gold, Weight 87.0 grams
Length 3⅛ in. Width 2¹⁄₁₆ in.

The primary form of this sonorous pendant is the sea turtle, its flippers given considerable detailing. The head has the raptorial beak and prominent eyes of bird-form pendants from the area, thus evoking two realms of potency, the sky as well as the water. Much wear to the sounding pellet and within the rattle chamber indicates the pendant's extensive use after it was made. The rear proper left flipper shows incomplete casting, resulting in an unintended beaded edge. The condition is good.

The lot is sold with a statement of authenticity from the distinguished expert Robert Sonin.

Provenance
Charles Craig, Santa Barbara

Estimate: $8,000-$12,000

47089

COLLAR WITH BEADED EDGES

Veraguas, Chiriquí, Diquís
A.D. 700/800–1500
Gold, Weight 182.9 grams
Height 8 1/16 in. Width 10 1/16 in.

The small neck opening of this massive semi-circular ornament suggests that it may have been a breast ornament rather than a collar. The careful spacing of the beading and the degree of finish given the paired suspension holes indicate the work of a fine craftsman. This is further confirmed by the even distribution and depth of the hammer peen marks still visible on the unburnished back. Similar status-indicative ornaments had a wide geographic distribution, but the context of this example in the group of gold pieces originally assembled by Charles Craig suggests the regional attribution assigned here. In addition to age patination there are numerous small surface scratches and some small ancient patches. There are two cracks, one at the inside proper right rim and one at just proper left of center on the outside rim.

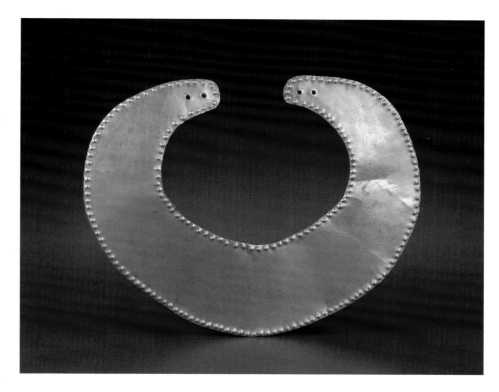

The lot is sold with a statement of authenticity from the distinguished expert Robert Sonin.

Provenance
Charles Craig, Santa Barbara

Estimate: $6,000-$9,000

47090

REPOUSSÉ DISK OF FROG

Veraguas, Chiriquí, Diquís
A.D. 700–1500
Gold, Weight 5.95 grams
Height 2 7/16 in. Width 2 7/16 in.

The imagery and ornamentation of this relatively small repoussé disk is worked so densely across the surface that any play of light produces an overall shimmering effect. Seen from above, a round-bodied toad is covered with raised spots and displays all four large legs. A repoussé circle frames this image, with a double row of closely-spaced beading filling the space to the edge of the disk. A tear extends inward from the right attachment hole as viewed from the front. Several cracks are visible in the lower center, possibly from ancient folding.

The lot is sold with statement of authenticity from the distinguished expert Robert Sonin.

Provenance
Charles Craig, Santa Barbara

Estimate: $1,500-$2,500

47091

PENDANT: BIRD WITH HUMAN ARMS

Veraguas, Chiriquí
A.D. 700–1500
Tumbaga, Weight 67.6 grams
Height 3⅜ in. Width 2⁵⁄₁₆ in.

Cast in high quality *tumbaga* rather than gold, this bell-shaped bird has a broad, hooked beak which touches the belly. Human arms rest against the upper belly, behind which small downward-curving hooks replace wings. Hooks similar to those by the body hang from the curving tips of the simple, three-part headdress. Prominent legs and three-toed bird feet project in front of the tail. Condition is fair: there are losses along the edges of headdress, "wing" hooks, and tail, and the proper left tip of the tail is missing, with further bending and cracking near the ends.

The lot is sold with a statement of authenticity from the distinguished expert Robert Sonin.

Provenance
Charles Craig, Santa Barbara

Estimate: $8,000-$12,000

47092

DOUBLE BIRD PENDANT

Veraguas, Chiriquí, Diquís
A.D. 700–1520
Gold, Weight 66.1 grams
Height 2¹¹⁄₁₆ in. Width 4³⁄₁₆ in.

Of sparely elegant design, this pendant has an unusually emphatic horizontal extension given by the widely spread shared tail, and the sharp-edged, pointed wings. The only ornamentation is a braided band laid on the lower edge of each wing. The heads are more animal than bird-like, which with the doubling of image suggests a shamanic transformational meaning. The gold is pinkish in color. Condition is good.

The lot is sold with a statement of authenticity from the distinguished expert Robert Sonin.

Provenance
Charles Craig, Santa Barbara

Estimate: $6,000-$9,000

47093

BIRD-FORM PENDANT

Veraguas or Chiriquí
A.D. 700–1500
Gold, Weight 82.8 grams
Height 4½ in. Width 4¾ in.

A severely elegant simplicity characterizes this pendant, whose chin-strap and shortened beak combine with the ridged raising of the body to suggest an influence from the Jalaca style. Various curl configurations emanate from the head, possibly derived from the curling crests of either a large raptor or the curasow. A small notch at the tip of the proper left tail was lost in the original hammering. The condition is good.

The lot is sold with a statement of authenticity from the distinguished expert Robert Sonin.

Provenance
Charles Craig, Santa Barbara

Estimate: $12,000-$18,000

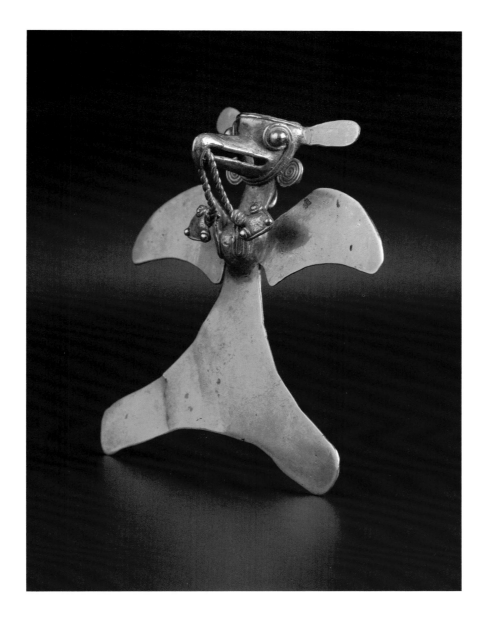

47094

BIRD-FORM PENDANT

Diquís, Veraguas, Chiriquí
A.D. 700/800–1520
Gold, Weight 106.31 grams
Height 4⅛ in. Width 4¹⁄₁₆ in.

This flat-headed bird holds a double-headed serpent with braided body in its beak. It also grasps the serpent just behind the heads with its talons. Flattened, rather narrow flanges extend to either side from the top of the head. A chin strap which extends to encircle the eyes relates to examples in the Jalaca style. In addition to curls at the ear area, the flat head is finished on the top in an open work pattern. A crease with top crack lies across the proper right tail flange; this, a wing crease, and other linear reflective patterns suggest that the piece may have been "killed." Overall condition is good, with two small blue stains.

The lot is sold with a statement of authenticity from the distinguished expert Robert Sonin.

Provenance
Charles Craig, Santa Barbara

Estimate: $8,000-$12,000

47095

DOUBLE-BIRD PENDANT

Azuero Peninsula
A.D. 200/300 – 700
Gold, Weight 79.91 grams
Height 2¼ in. Width 3½ in.

The elegantly simplified head and beak with side-projecting eyes, combined with the strictly horizontal termination of the blade–like tail, indicate an early date for this pendant in the form of two partially fused birds. Often called "international," this style is found both in the northern and Caribbean areas of Colombia and in lower Central America, primarily Panama. It marks the move northward of the sophisticated gold casting techniques which had originated in what is now lower Colombia and northern Ecuador. The elaboration of the wing edges with a series of coils is unusual in the generally austere style. The condition is very good, with small veins visible from the back at both tips of the tail, the result of the hammering process used to complete the tail, which produces a delicate surface dimpling on the reverse.

The lot is sold with a statement of authenticity from the distinguished expert Robert Sonin.

Provenance
Charles Craig, Santa Barbara

Estimate: $8,000-$10,000

47096

BIRD-FORM PENDANT

Diquís Delta
A.D. 700–1500
Gold, Weight 133.66 grams
Height 3½ in. Width 3¾ in.

The special feature of this pendant is the substitution of a well-developed, eared feline head where body and talons would commonly be shown. The unusually rounded wings have raised bosses on their lower edges. Profile outward-facing crocodile heads flank the head, and the ear area is developed into simplified profile bird heads. The body contains a rattle chamber with pellet. The upper edges of the wings are ragged, and a small casting lapse hole is in the bottom center of the tail. A few stains are visible in body and head area, more so on the back.

The lot is sold with a statement of authenticity from the distinguished expert Robert Sonin.

Provenance
Charles Craig, Santa Barbara

Estimate: $16,000-$20,000

47097

BIRD-FORM PENDANT

Diquís
A.D. 700–1500
Gold, Weight 178.8 grams
Height 4½ in. Width 4 in.

The overall effect of this pendant is almost Spartan, in part
caused by the long neck and simplified treatment of most details.
The rather thin-beaked head is flanked by curl-headed profile
zoomorphs, while the ear ornaments are profile bird heads. Small
casting fins have been left where wings and tail meet. Current
condition is good.

The lot is sold with a statement of authenticity from the
distinguished expert Robert Sonin.

Provenance
Charles Craig, Santa Barbara

Estimate: $15,000-$18,000

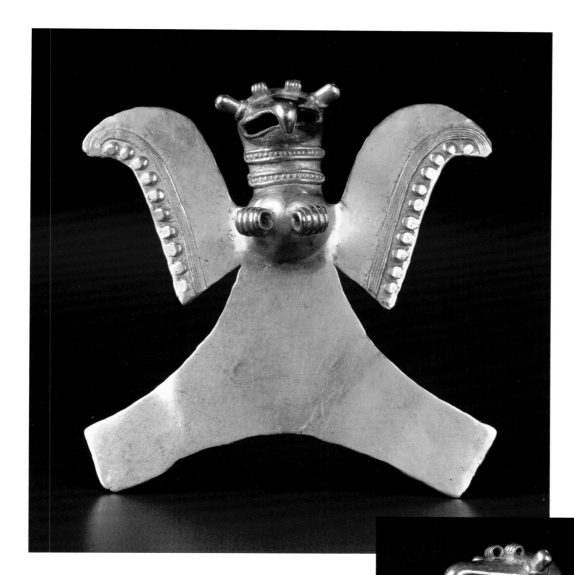

47098

BIRD-FORM PENDANT

Diquís or Veraguas
A.D. 700–1500
Gold, Weight 135.6 grams
Height 4½ in. Width 3¼ in.

Several unusual features are present on this bird-form pendant. The wings arch high and stay close to the body, there is a slight tilt to the head, and the feet torque in relation to the body. The stalk eyes retain an early stylistic feature, while the outer band-and-boss wing enhancements are reminiscent of Jalaca style. The braided suspension loop is also unusual. Two folds across the tail, one with an incipient crack system at the lower edge, suggest that the pendant may have been ritually "killed" at some point in time. Condition is otherwise good.

The lot is sold with a statement of authenticity from the distinguished expert Robert Sonin.

Provenance
Charles Craig, Santa Barbara

Estimate: $12,000-$15,000

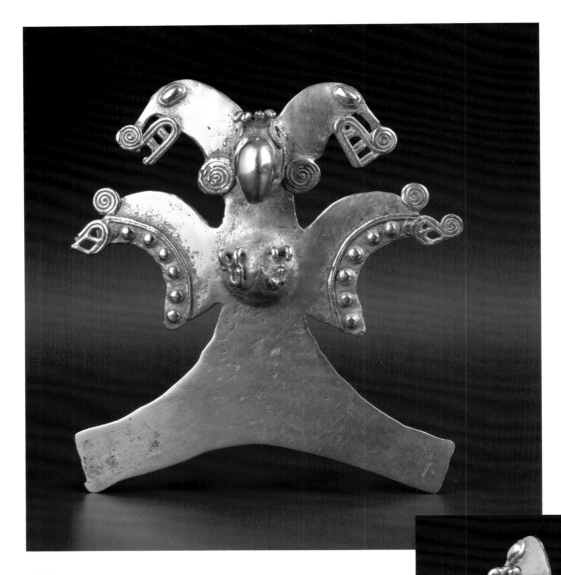

47099

BIRD-FORM PENDANT

Diquís Delta
A.D. 700–1500
Gold, Weight 135.45 grams
Height 4½ in. Width 4³⁄₃₂ in.

Bold, lively profile crocodile heads arch at either side above the massively-beaked bird whose spiky crest may indicate that it is a harpy eagle, the largest and most powerful New World raptor. The heavy, broad beak and chin strap around the eye are characteristics of the Jalaca region style. The talon treatment, with its suggestion of front and rear opposition, is unusual. The beaded wings are given a further powerful enhancement by small, profile crocodile heads at their tips. There is a crack in the proper left tail, with the condition otherwise good.

The lot is sold with a statement of authenticity from the distinguished expert Robert Sonin.

Provenance
Charles Craig, Santa Barbara

Estimate: $16,000-$20,000

47100

BIRD-FORM PENDANT

Diquís Delta
A.D. 700–1500
Gold, Weight 132.01 grams
Height 4⁵⁄₁₆ in. Width 3¹³⁄₁₆ in.

This heavy casting portrays a raptorial bird with especially massive beak and talons, the latter arrayed in a menacing row across the body. Supernatural elements include a three-part, clawlike frontal crest and outward facing, open-mouthed profile zoomorphs at either side of the head. The lower edges of the spread wings are each accented by four bosses enclosed by an arced double band. S-shaped curls at ear position and a double chin strap which coils around the eyes complete the image. This chin strap and the massive beak are characteristics of the Jalaca style region of the Diquís Delta. The condition is excellent, with ancient manufacturing fills visible on the flared tail.

The lot is sold with a statement of authenticity from the distinguished expert Robert Sonin

Provenance
Charles Craig, Santa Barbara

Estimate: $16,000-$20,000

47101

DOUBLE-HEADED BIRD-FORM PENDANT

Diquís
A.D. 700–1500
Gold, Weight 178.57 grams
Height 4 1/16 in. Width 4 7/16 in.

This richly elaborated pendant has not only double, crested bird heads, but two-tiered profile crocodile heads extending to the sides from behind the bird heads, their necks emanating sequences of curls. Great visual dynamism results. The braiding which surrounds the bosses along the lower wing edges supplements the energy of the composition. Suspension hooks were cast from the beak tips and ends of the talons, but there is no evidence that danglers were ever provided. The pendant was ritually "killed," fortunately not with great severity, but still enough to crack and bend the talons and blunt the curls at the upper beak tips and the beak-end suspension hooks. This process also flattened the back suspension loop. An ancient patch was integrated into the proper left tail end by hammering. The condition is good.

The lot is sold with a statement of authenticity from the distinguished expert Robert Sonin.

Provenance
Charles Craig, Santa Barbara

Estimate: $20,000-$25,000

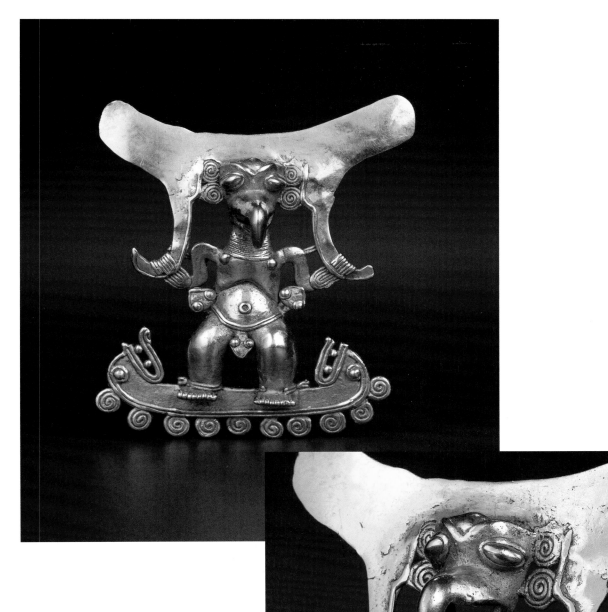

47102

PENDANT: STANDING SUPERNATURAL

Veraguas or Diquís
A.D. 700–1500
Gold, Weight 110.2 grams
Height 3¾ in. Width 3⁵⁄₁₆ in.

This massive, raptor-beaked anthropomorph stands on a flattened crescent-shaped bar with profile upward-facing snake heads at either end. From its outer, double-banded edge ten evenly-spaced curls emerge. The male figure wears a waist band terminating in outward facing serpent heads and has a serpent-head penis sheath. His extended hands grasp the curved ends of dependencies fusing with his broad, flattened headdress. Double curls are at the ear areas. The nipples, rib cage, and navel are given unusual prominence in this unusually sculptural figure. The condition is excellent.

The lot is sold with a statement of authenticity from the distinguished expert Robert Sonin.

Provenance
Charles Craig, Santa Barbara

Estimate: $12,000-$15,000

47103

ARTICULATED PENDANT, SUPERNATURAL TWO-HEADED BIRD

Diquís
A.D. 700–1500
Gold, Weight 192.72 grams
Height 3¹⁵/₁₆ in. Width 3⁵/₈ in.

This bird–form pendant is distinguished by its very rarely seen articulated double heads flanked by profile supernatural zoomorphs. These latter with open, toothed mouths have spiralled bubble forms along both tops and bottoms of their necks. The bird heads have curled frontal crests, and their downward-curving upper beaks fuse into hooks as well as having loops at the point of curvature. Massive feet on the rattle chamber body have five talons on each foot, below which hang two more large hooks. The rattle is gone from the body chamber, and lack of wear on any of the hooks suggests that danglers may never have been added. Articulation served to animate further the spirit content of such images, and the doubling of heads probably implied a range of dualities embodied by the portrayed supernatural. A closely similar example is one of the treasures of Costa Rica's Museo del Oro Precolombino. The condition is excellent.

The lot is sold with a statement of authenticity from the distinguished expert Robert Sonin.

Provenance
Charles Craig, Santa Barbara

Estimate: $30,000-$40,000

47104

SUPERNATURAL ANIMAL PENDANT

Veraguas, Chiriquí
A.D. 900–1520
Gold, Weight 236.83 grams
Height 1⅞ in. Length 4⁷⁄₁₆ in.

Cast so that it would hang vertically, this pendant is designed so that each animal head turns to the wearer's right. The full animal is primarily feline in its characteristics, but the nose area is that of a tapir. The long feline tail terminates in a smaller head which similarly combines both tapir and feline elements. The way in which both heads are animated by tilt, ear position, and open mouth shows that the ancient artisan was an astute observer. Further, the fanned claws suggest a feline just landing from a pounce. A band of triangular openings down the spine introduces a crocodilian overtone (these are all filled with what are known as casting fins, where shrinking of the clay and charcoal investment allowed an unwanted flow of gold). The condition is excellent.

The lot is sold with a statement of authenticity from the distinguished expert Robert Sonin.

Provenance
Charles Craig, Santa Barbara

Estimate: $16,000-$20,000

47105

**PENDANT: JAGUAR WITH A
HUMAN LEG IN ITS MOUTH**

Veraguas, Chiriquí, Diquís
A.D. 900−1520
Gold, Weight 54.51 grams
Length 2⅝ in. Width 1⅝ in.

A sleekly sculptural jaguar with an almost playful look
holds a human leg in its mouth, the foot at the animal's
right side and a bit of fleshed bone end at the left.
Several similar examples are known, including one in
the Fundación Museos Banco Central de Costa Rica
(BCCR9), San José. The condition is good.

The lot is sold with a statement of authenticity from
the distinguished expert Robert Sonin.

Provenance
Charles Craig, Santa Barbara

Estimate: $6,000-$9,000

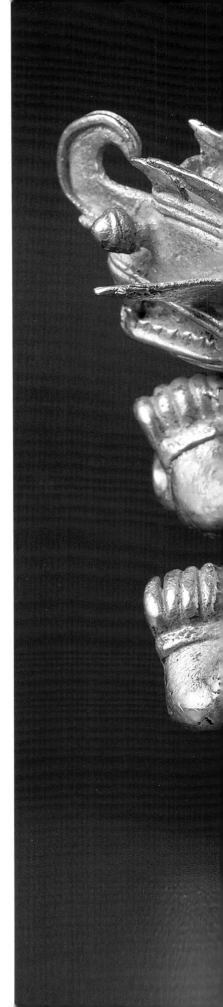

47106

MASSIVE PENDANT OF JOINED, CRESTED SUPERNATURALS

Coclé/Parita, Macaracas Phase
A.D. 800–1100
Gold, Weight 462.0 grams
Height 4⅛ in. Width 4¾ in.

In every way—conceptually, aesthetically, and technically—this is a masterpiece of the ancient gold worker's art. Two joined supernatural quadrupeds (of the type commonly called "crested crocodiles") with alert, out-turned heads strain against one another, their tense energy visibly embodied in this image. Upraised tails balance the large, squared off heads. The heads combine features from symbolic animals: the upturned nose and pointed ears of the bat, a primarily feline snarling mouth, and scutiform crocodilian crests. Bats are creatures of the sky and night; jaguars inhabit both earth and water as well as being active both day and night; and crocodiles, primarily underwater inhabitants, do come on the earth to sun, and in many New World mythic systems represent the Earth. The joining of two such potent beings by shared feet suggests dualities that are at once complementary and opposing. The small curled spirals on the necks are unusual, and might be intended to evoke the bubbling surface of water as the creatures move from one cosmological level to another. The addition of bands just above the feet and braided waist bands further bridges the worlds of humans, animals, and supernaturals. The right ear of the being at the viewer's left is bent, and there is a casting separation below the waist band of the right supernatural. Otherwise, the condition is excellent.

The lot is sold with a statement of authenticity from the distinguished expert Robert Sonin.

Provenance
Charles Craig, Santa Barbara

Estimate: $50,000-$80,000

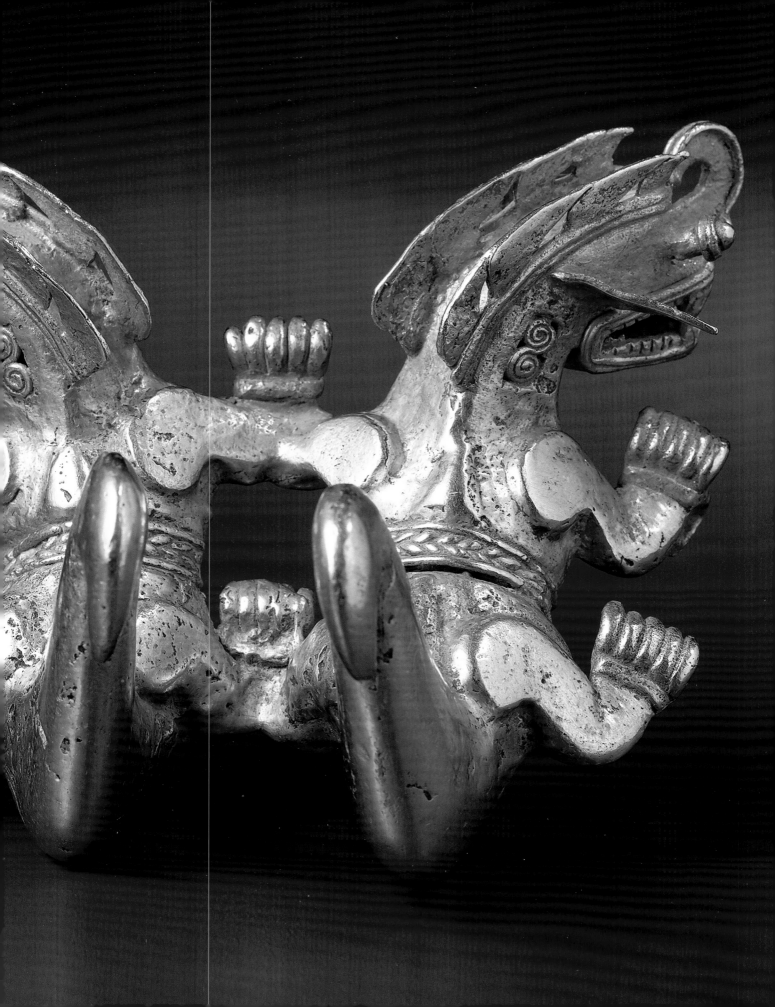

47107

PENDANT: MYTHICAL ANIMAL

Veraguas or Diquís
A.D. 900–1500
Gold, Weight 168.96 grams
Height 4⁵⁄₁₆ in. Width 3½ in.

A mythicized female animal is shown in displayed posture with its toothed, dog-like head projecting boldly outward from the large trapezoidal headdress. This latter has somewhat randomly placed triangular openings over most of its expanse, with terminating profile zoomorphs at the lower corners. The upturned noses of these heads and those which terminate the bifurcated tail suggest bats of the leaf-nosed family. S-shaped spirals form ears. All the paws show forward- curling toes. The waist emanations suggest shark fins, which might provide a water reference to go with the main creature's earth orientation and the bats' aerial habitat to give a complete three-level cosmological representation. The condition is excellent.

The lot is sold with a statement of authenticity from the distinguished expert Robert Sonin.

Provenance
Charles Craig, Santa Barbara

Estimate: $16,000-$20,000

47108

PENDANT: FANTASTIC ANIMAL

Veraguas, Chiriquí
A.D. 900–1520
Gold, Weight 106.91 grams
Length 3⁵⁄₁₆ in. Height 1¾ in.

Bird, animal, and amphibian elements combine to create this fantastic creature which thus embodies the three major cosmological levels. The basic quadruped form has flippers in lieu of feet, and, though toothed, has the overall head of a crested bird as well as a bird tail. The use of beads to form the teeth is unusual. The image is completed by the four openwork triangles which mark the spine, probably a reference to another important symbolic creature, the crocodile. The condition is excellent.

The lot is sold with a statement of authenticity from the distinguished expert Robert Sonin.

Provenance
Charles Craig, Santa Barbara

Estimate: $10,000-$15,000

47109

PENDANT: STANDING DEITY

Veraguas, Chiriquí, or Diquís
A.D. 700–1500
Gold, Weight 66.6 grams
Height 3⅜ in. Width 3 3/16 in.

The frontal format of this pendant preserves considerable symmetry: the flanged headdress balances the broad, long-oval flange on which the deity stands; the upside-down profile animal heads at the lower parts of the headdress correspond to upright profile heads flanking the figure's spread legs; and the squared-off shoulders and rounded elbows create a central balancing area which complements forms immediately above and below. When seen from above, the flattened zoomorphic head is formed by banded strips crossing an open area. Bulging eyes, a curled nose, and full-toothed mouth give an alert but surprisingly benign expression to the male deity, which holds a coiled plant in each hand. Curls beside the head with open ear loops below, a banded necklace, and a several strand waistband complete the image. The condition is very good.

The lot is sold with a statement of authenticity from the distinguished expert Robert Sonin.

Provenance
Charles Craig, Santa Barbara

Estimate: $18,000-24,000

47110

**PENDANT: SUPERNATURAL SHAMANIC FIGURE
WITH PADDLE-SHAPED CLUBS**

Coclé Province or Azuero Peninsula
A.D. 650–1520
Gold, Weight 82.425 grams
Height 2¾ in. Width 2⁹⁄₁₆ in.

Single figures wielding two paddle-clubs are less common than paired club-bearers. This individual has a bat-like nose, with nose plug, and bat ears, with eyes protruding on stalks suggestive of the ability to see beyond the ordinary. The unusual and elaborate headdress is so wholly conventionalized that it is uncertain what additional spirit helpers are indicated. In what is probably a development from actual ritual clothing, large concave units at the waist connect with downward curved shapes and triangular pieces to form abbreviated crocodilian profiles which connect to the bottom of each club handle. These too were spirit-supporters of the central figure. The condition is excellent.

The lot is sold with a statement of authenticity from the distinguished expert Robert Sonin.

Provenance
Charles Craig, Santa Barbara

Estimate: $8,000-$12,000

47111

TWIN FIGURE PENDANT

Coclé Province or Azuero Peninsula
A.D. 650–1520
Gold, Weight 95.05 grams
Height 1⅞ in. Width 3¹³⁄₁₆ in.

The heraldically frontal figures stand on a single bar, and a further connection is made in the upper center where their fists meet, each clasping a bundled object ending in a small curled top (possibly a spear thrower). Each holds a large paddle-shaped club in the outer hand. A supernatural, trance-like, state is shown by bulging eyes and grimacing mouths along with bat noses and ears. Each has coiled ear ornaments and wears a simple loin cloth. The powerful composition is completed by downward-curving emanations from either side of both waists, their internal crocodilian notches somewhat obscured by casting fins. The massively sculptural execution seen here is exceptional, adding further power to this compelling double image illustrating duality. The condition is excellent.

The lot is sold with a statement of authenticity from the distinguished expert Robert Sonin.

Provenance
Charles Craig, Santa Barbara

Estimate: $16,000-$18,000

47112

PENDANT: SHAMAN HOLDING RATTLES

Veraguas, Chiriquí, Diquís
A.D. 700–1500
Gold, Weight 84.1 grams
Height 3¹⁄₁₆ in. Width 2³⁄₈ in.

The flexed legs of this shaman along with the rattles he holds in each hand indicate participation in a ceremonial dance. This is further supported by the concentrated, trance-like expression and the fact that the knee and ankle bindings may have had attached bells. The tooth-like, rayed headdress and huge ear-flaps enhance the sense of a ritualized context. A beaded and banded necklace completes the garb. The casting is rough in several places, especially at the jointure points of legs to body and the neck area, but overall condition is good. A bar rather than the more usual loop is provided for suspension.

The lot is sold with a statement of authenticity from the distinguished expert Robert Sonin.

Provenance
Charles Craig, Santa Barbara

Estimate: $16,000-$18,000

47113

PENDANT: MALE SHAMAN HOLDING RATTLES

Veraguas or Chiriquí
A.D 700–1500
Tumbaga, Weight 110.1 grams
Height 4¼ in. Width 2³⁄₁₆ in.

Unusually ambitious and sculptural for a *tumbaga* casting, this quite naturalistic figure echoes the still-influential Quimbaya figural style of Colombia, even though it probably originated some centuries later than the high point of that group of gold pieces. The fully naked shaman with semi-seated posture is a further Quimbaya derivation. The figure holds large rattles, which probably once had pellets themselves, and has a banded collar. His trance-ridden expression combines with the headdress and double-spiral flaps at the sides of his head to indicate his being in the midst of a shamanic ritual event. There is some cracking at edges and slight scaling, both inherent with *tumbaga*.

The lot is sold with a statement of authenticity from the distinguished expert Robert Sonin.

Provenance
Charles Craig, Santa Barbara

Estimate: $8,000-$12,000

47114

SHAMAN PENDANT

Diquís Delta Area
A.D. 700–1500
Gold, Weight 114.18 grams
Height 3 1/16 in. Width 4 1/16 in.

His posture defiantly frontal with flexed arms and legs, this bold figure almost certainly depicts a shaman during his spirit flight. He grasps the inner body of an encircling double-headed serpentine creature whose lower, outer body bristles with trapezoidal scutes, exaggerations of those on a mature crocodile (these also indicate an awareness of the important Coclé power center in Panama, where such forms are a major iconographic feature). A ropelike cord passes from his wrists across his naked body, some form of power conduit related to the braided forms which emanate from his mouth to connect with the five birds which ride the shaman's head. These birds would have been the shaman's spirit messengers and conveyors during his own flights. The curl-terminated snouts of two creatures extend from the shaman's ears to his shoulders. In many areas the shaman is naked during the most intense trance communication, thus becoming a fully open receptor of spirit forces. The condition is excellent, with visible age patination.

The lot is sold with a statement of authenticity from the distinguished expert Robert Sonin.

Provenance
Charles Craig, Santa Barbara

Estimate: $18,000-$24,000

COLOMBIA AND EQUADOR

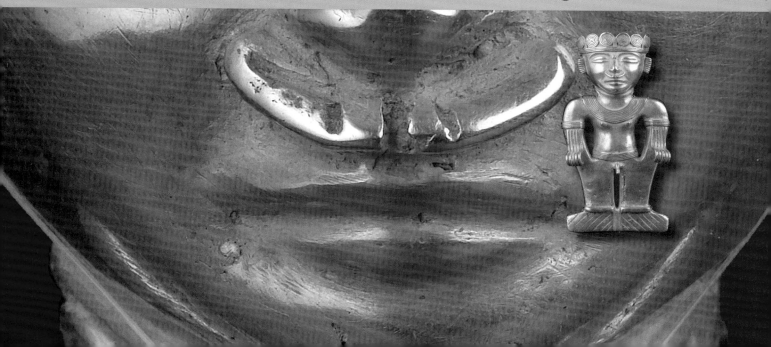

47115

STANDING MALE FIGURE

Calima
100 B.C.–A.D. 400
Burnished ceramic
Height 12½ in. Width 9 in.

The radically stylized male figure is incised over much of the body with geometric patterns which probably represent body painting. He has a bulky circular nose ornament and holes in the ear area where ornaments could have been affixed. The unusually shaped legs probably represent tight cord binding which is still done among remnant indigenous groups in the lowlands of Colombia and the greater Amazon watershed. No similar published examples have been found, and the traditional Calima attribution seems reasonable. The condition is very good except for a minor replacement on the proper left foot.

Provenance
William Siegal, Santa Fe, New Mexico

Estimate: $4,000-$6,000

47116

CONVEX FACE MASK

Calima
100 B.C.–A.D. 400
Burnished ceramic, traces of white paint
Height 10 in. Width 11⅜ in.

This large and striking face mask is covered with deeply incised patterns which include profile zoomorphic heads that most resemble crocodilian or serpentine images. Four of these heads form a framing crest around the upper head and two outward-facing examples fill the chin area. In combination with possible variant inward-facing forms at either side of the mouth, these serve to enclose the face within their field of influence. Small circles filled with white pigment create a secondary framing rhythm. Within the overall highly stylized representation a surprisingly naturalistic nose is developed in a strongly three-dimensional manner.

The regional attribution seems convincing, and a seemingly related example is illustrated in Armand J. Labbé, *Shamans, Gods, and Mythic Beasts: Colombian Gold and Ceramics in Antiquity*. New York: The American Federation of Arts,1998 (p.126, fig.2). Other than minor frontal abrasions and some vertical scratches on the back, the condition is very good.

Provenance
Alfredo Ocampo, Calí, Colombia
William Siegal Galleries, Santa Fe: 2004 catalogue, item 62.

Published
Siegal, William. *Pre-Columbian Art*. Santa Fe: William Siegal Galleries, 2004.

Estimate: $10,000-$14,000

47117

EFFIGY VESSEL

Yotoco
A.D. 100–800
Ceramic
Height 8½ in. Width 5¾ in.

This vessel shape with twin spouts separated by a strap-handle is typical of Yotoco Phase ceramics. Although pre-European Colombia is best known for its gold work, there is a rich ceramic tradition with a long history. Many of these pieces are as much fully-realized small-sized sculptures as vessels, which is the case here. The rhythmically-developed body of this seated figure gains its formal coherence by conforming to the basic pot shape, enhanced by the maker's ability to inhabit these shapes with an inner, animating energy. The elaborate nose ornament shows a common use of gold, and the D-shaped eyes are a wide-spread convention in southern Colombia during the first millennium of our era. Cracks have been slightly filled, but there are no replacement areas. There is minor surface pitting, mainly on the back of the head, and there are some manganese oxide deposits.

Provenance
David Bernstein, New York

Estimate: $5,000-$6,000

47118

LARGE BURIAL URN WITH HUMAN HALF-FIGURE ON LID

Sinú (?)
A.D. 1200–1500
Buff ceramic
Lid: Height 16 in.   Diameter 10½ in.
Urn: Height 15½ in.   Diameter 12½ in.

The alertly-posed female half-figure is formally closest to published examples in the Moskito Style of the lower Magdalena River region in greater Sinú. Wearing only earspools and a nose ornament, the figure has closely cropped hair in a cap-like style. Such large globular jars were used for secondary burials. The forehead has a small patch, and there are cracks and chips along with light surface stain and abrasions on the lid. The urn was broken in a number of pieces and has been reassembled with some fill.

Provenance

Bonhams & Butterfields, San Francisco: sale 7437E, 9 June 2003, lot 5029, p.10

Estimate: $3,000-$4,000

47119

BURIAL URN WITH SEATED FEMALE FIGURE HOLDING A CUP

Sinú (?)
A.D. 1200–1500
Brown ceramic, white pigment
Lid: Height 12¼ in.   Diameter 9¾ in.
Urn: Height 19 in.   Diameter 16 in.

The lid of this large burial urn is topped with a seated female figure holding a cup. The rendering of the fingers of both hands is most unusual, looking more like attached ornaments than integral body components. The head and general body treatment suggest a middle Magdalena River valley origin. The incised geometric designs on the sides of the lid continue onto the shoulder of the urn itself. These have been filled with white pigment. The domed lid was shattered into thirteen pieces, which have been reassembled with some filling. The top of the head has repairs and the ears of the figure are abraded from insertion of ear ornaments. There is minor cracking on the left of the torso. The bottom one-fourth of the urn has water staining and encrustations.

Provenance

Bonhams & Butterfields, San Francisco: sale 7437E, 9 June 2003, lot 5028, p.10

Estimate: $3,000-$4,000

47120

ANTHROPOMORPHIC IMAGE

Chorrera (?)
ca. 1000 – 300 B.C.
Stone
Height 14⅞ in. Width 5⅞ in.

This enigmatic, highly abstracted anthropomorphic figure is among the larger examples from a group of unprovenanced stone images. With the single exception of an example illustrated by Hernán Crespo Toral and Olaf Holm (*Arte Precolombino de Ecuador.* Quito: Salvat Editores Ecuatoriana S.A. 1977, p.90) and credited as Chorrera, all the other published examples call the images "Valdivia." Our research suggests that this has no basis in the archaeological literature. Published Valdivia stone images do not resemble this and the like examples in style or technique, and, most importantly, there are radical size discrepancies between the minute Valdivia examples and all pieces resembling the present image. There are several surface cracks, none severe or marring the visual and physical integrity of this striking sculpture.

Provenance
Bonhams & Butterfields, San Francisco: sale 7477E, 8 December 2003, lot 3024

Estimate: $6,000-$8,000

47121

FOUR FIGURAL *TUNJOS*

Muisca
A.D. 900–1500
Tumbaga, Weight 26 grams
Height (tallest) 3⅜ in. Height (shortest) 2¹³⁄₁₆ in.

Tunjos survive by the thousands from the Muisca, the group which at the time of the Spanish incursion inhabited the high plateau in the area of modern Bogotá. Their use paralleled that of modern *ex votos*. Pilgrims to shrines could purchase *tunjos* with iconography suited to each individual's needs. These were then placed as offerings, frequently in ceramic vessels set at special sacred locations. Each of the present four portrays a conventionalized standing figure, one holding a bow, with arrows in the right hand. Another presents a bowl with both hands. The other two hold a flat club and a *poporo* and lime dipper respectively. Other than minute casting flaws, the condition of all four figures is very good.

Provenance
Christie's, Paris: sale 5068, 10 December 2003, lot 454, p.135

Estimate: $5,000-$6,000

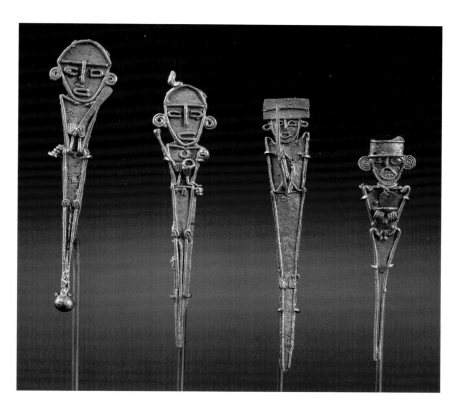

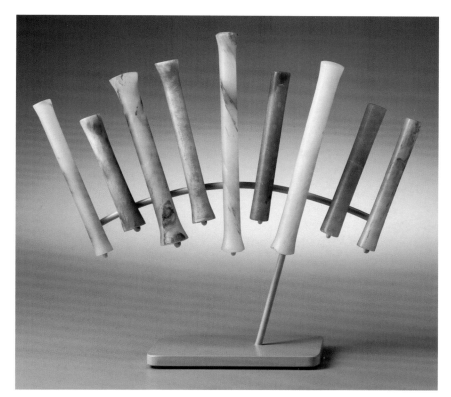

47122

NINE LARGE TUBULAR BEADS

Tairona
A.D. 1000–1500
Stone
Height (smallest) 2⅞ in. Height (tallest) 5⅛ in.

This is an assemblage of nine hard stone tubular beads, which were components of Tairona jewelry. Four are red-orange carnelian and five are of a white stone with gray clouds. The shapes vary from virtually straight-sided to subtly flared at both ends. All have an excellent polish. One has a crack line at its center point.

Provenance
Daniel F. McLister, Santa Fe, New Mexico

Estimate: $1,000-$1,500

47123

LIME DIPPER WITH STANDING SHAMAN

Yotoco
A.D. 100–800
Gold, Weight 58 grams
Height 10 in. Width 1³/₁₆ in. Height (figure) 1³/₈ in.

This cast lime dipper is capped by a standing shaman wearing a
large-eyed, open-mouthed mask with a notched lower edge. He
has looped ear areas and a high backward-curving cap. He holds a
shaman's staff with both hands. he staff and the figure's upper arms,
legs, and back are all patterned with incised cross-hatching. Lime
dippers were used in connection with gourd or metal containers
which held the powdered mineral lime necessary as a catalyst in
chewing coca leaves. The dipper tip was moistened so that the
requisite small amount of lime would adhere. As the dipper was
not polished after casting, the surface is slightly porous in places.
Minute dirt residues remain on several parts of the finial image.

Provenance
David Walley, Pontotoc, Mississippi

Estimate: $5,000-$6,000

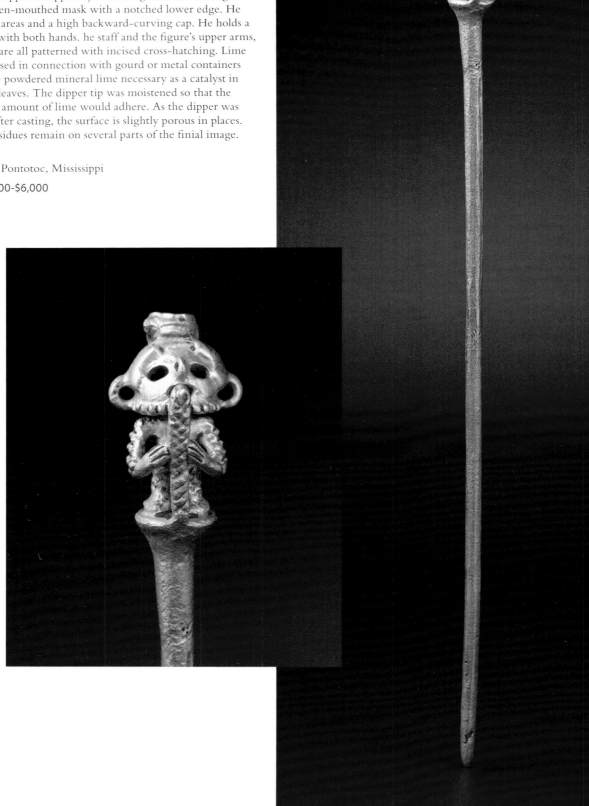

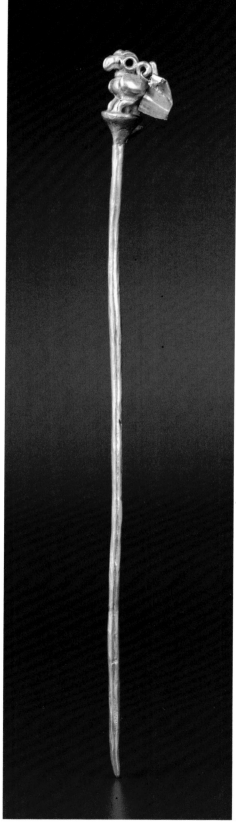

47124

LIME DIPPER WITH BIRD FINIAL

Yotoco
A.D. 100–800
Gold, Weight 40 grams
Height 7⅞ in. Depth ¹³⁄₁₆ in. Height (bird) ¾ in.

An alert-looking bird with curved beak and rippled crest stands on the flared area at the top of the dipper shaft. Beak and crest suggest that this may represent a harpy eagle. Two integrally-cast loops attached on the wings have rectangular sheets of metal foil attached with wires. A small center element curves upward from the back near the base of the tail. Fine lime dippers would have been the prerogative of someone of rank and power. The condition is very good.

Provenance
David Walley, Pontotoc, Mississippi
Christie's Paris, vente: 5068/441

Estimate: $5,000-$6,000

117

47125

TALL BLADE-SHAPED BREAST PLATE

Calima
200 B.C.–A.D. 200
Gold
Height 16 in. Width 9⅟₁₆ in.

This important tall blade-shaped pectoral has repoussé human faces at top and bottom. The upper silhouette flares outward in two elements which end in knobs. The upper face is delimited by diagonal lines at the temples and a broad raised chin line. The lower reverses the procedure with an arced brow line and slightly curved diagonals at the cheek areas. Each face is comprised of an interlocked eyebrow-nose unit, oval eyes, ears shaped like question marks, and an oval mouth with bared teeth. Two punches at top center were for attachment. The back of the pectoral shares with one published example (Colin McEwan. *Precolumbian Gold Technology, Style and Iconography.* Chigago: Fitzroy Dearborn Publishers, 2000, p.102, fig. 5.12) the dark impression of multiple strands of small beads. The pectoral may have been folded near the bottom, and there are several small crack patterns.

Provenance
Dylan Graeme Collection
Wally and Brenda Zollman Collection, Indianapolis
Butterfields & Butterfields, San Francisco: sale 7307E, 25 March 2002, lot 5084 (QEL00.E.52), p.26, ill. p.26

Estimate: $8,000-$12,000

47126

PENDANT PROBABLY REPRESENTING A SHAMAN

Sinú
A.D. 100 – 700
Gold, Weight 40 grams
Height 4³⁄₁₆ in. Width 1¹⁵⁄₁₆ in.

This figure, representative of a type known from a number of Sinú examples, has three paired leaf-like forms along the elongated body which ended in an arrow-like form, the tip of which is now missing. He has a necklace of horizontal elements, spirals at the ears, and a symmetrical downward-curved double headdress, from the upper center of which rises a rectangular form with minute side indentations near the top. The overall effect of this image is strongly reminiscent of a growing maize plant. The condition is good, with minor surface deposits.

The lot is sold with a statement of authenticity from the distinguished expert Robert Sonin.

Provenance
David Bernstein, New York

Estimate: $6,000-$8,000

47127

TWO PENDANTS REPRESENTING SHAMANS

Sinú
A.D. 100 – 700
Gold, Weight 50 grams (total)
Height 2¼ in. Width 1³⁄₈ in.
Height 2¾ in. Width 1⁵⁄₈ in.

While not a pair, these two similar pendants are close to one another in size. The smaller one is a relatively rough casting in pinkish native gold, in which the surface forms are somewhat blurred. The headdress arcs to either side from a central wedge-shaped element, curling back to touch the ear areas. Its outer rims are edged with fine incised parallel lines. The figure has braided head and waist bands and a necklace of rectangular elements. Two downward-turned leaf-like forms are on either side of the elongated body, which ends in a bifurcated tip. A small globular casting fault extends from the proper right tip of the headdress. The condition is excellent.

The other shaman figure has two leaf-like forms at either side of the elongated body, which is crossed by horizontal bands above and below the lower pair of leaf forms. An imperfectly-cast arrow completes the lower tip. The points at the outer ends of the arced double headdress end in profile zoomorph heads. An upward-pointing arrow is at the top center, rising from a braided headband. Spiral ear ornaments and a complex necklace complete the attire. Other than several original casting faults, the condition is excellent.

The lot is sold with a statement of authenticity from the distinguished expert Robert Sonin.

Provenance
David Bernstein, New York

Estimate: $5,000-$7,000

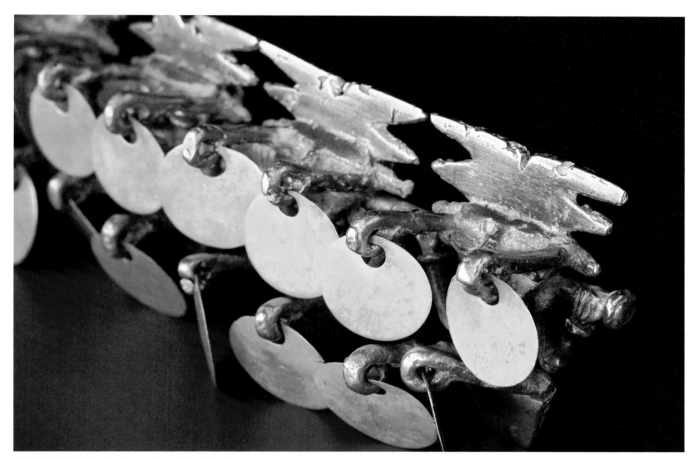

47128

LARGE BAR PECTORAL WITH SIX SHAMANIC FIGURES

Sinú
A.D. 100 – 700
Gold, Weight 308 grams
Height 1¾ in. Width 9³⁄₁₆ in.

This exceptionally large, pinkish gold bar pectoral would have virtually spanned the wearer's entire chest. Six shaman figures grasp with both hands the connecting bar. Their torsos end in a bifurcated point, and each wears a necklace and bracelets. Three-tiered headdresses suggestive of bird wings terminate at either side in points. Four circular danglers vibrate in front of each figure from integrally-cast loop extensions. The condition is excellent.

The lot is sold with a statement of authenticity from the distinguished expert Robert Sonin.

Provenance
David Bernstein, New York

Estimate: $20,000-$25,000

47129

HEAD-FORM BELL

Sinú
A.D. 400–1000
Gold, Weight 58 grams
Height 1⅝ in. Width 2¹³⁄₁₆ in.

This striking bell in the form of a
classic Sinú human face is a variant of a
configuration seen with some frequency:
a puffy-cheeked face with headband,
above which large outward-facing birds'
heads form the headdress. Spirals lie
where the ears are located. The condition
is good.

The lot is sold with a statement of
authenticity from the distinguished
expert Robert Sonin.

Provenance
David Bernstein, New York

Estimate: $10,000-$15,000

47130

HEAD-FORM BELL

Sinú
A.D. 400–1000
Gold, Weight 164 grams
Height 2½ in. Width 4 in.

With all of its circular danglers in place,
this pendant bell retains its original
appearance. These danglers hide the
mouth, the ear spirals, and all but the
outward-extending beaks of the addorsed
headdress birds' heads. When worn,
the moving danglers would have set
up an ever-changing array of vibrant
reflections. The condition is good.

The lot is sold with a statement of
authenticity from the distinguished
expert Robert Sonin.

Provenance
David Bernstein, New York

Estimate: $10,000-$15,000

47131

HEAD-FORM BELL

Sinú
A.D. 400–1000
Gold, Weight 126 grams
Height 2⅛ in. Width 3⅛ in.

A face that is large in relation to the
outward-facing birds' heads that form a
crown above it gives this pendant bell an
aggressive look. This is reinforced by the
rigidly horizontal, thin lips. A braided
headband and spirals at the ear area
complete the integrally cast décor. Five
circular danglers suspended from cast
loops conceal the birds' heads. A dangler
remains attached to the proper left ear;
both those at the other ear and the nose,
for which loops were cast, are missing.
The condition is very good.

The lot is sold with a statement of
authenticity from the distinguished
expert Robert Sonin.

Provenance
David Bernstein, New York

Estimate: $10,000-$15,000

47132

HEAD-FORM BELL

Sinú
A.D. 400–1000
Gold, Weight 86 grams
Height 2 in. Width 3⅝ in.

With its fuller, more modeled lips
and eyes, this head-form bell differs
slightly from the other examples in the
Hendershott Collection. Otherwise,
it retains the braided headband, spiral
ear areas, and outward-facing birds'
heads that are seen on the others. Three
circular danglers are in front of the
central headdress, with two others at
either ear spiral. The condition is good.

The lot is sold with a statement of
authenticity from the distinguished
expert Robert Sonin.

Provenance
David Bernstein, New York

Estimate: $10,000-$15,000

47133

TWO NOSE ORNAMENTS

Sinú
A.D. 400–1000
Gold, Weight of both 94 grams
(A) Height 3 in. Width 3⅞ in.
(B) Height 1½ in Width 7¹⁵⁄₁₆ in.

Both ornaments are worked in heavy gold. One is a bold, full oval disk with a small circular opening below the septum area. The other was attached with a smaller, more circular disk from either side of which extend long gold bars, each containing five circular danglers suspended from integrally-cast loops. This more complex ornament has some adhering reddish deposits, primarily on the back. Such large, showy nose ornaments were part of the status-asserting regalia of important Sinú individuals.

The lot is sold with a statement of authenticity from the distinguished expert Robert Sonin.

Provenance
David Bernstein, New York

Estimate: $6,000-$8,000

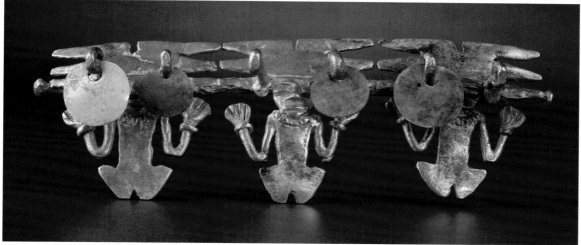

47134

BAR PECTORAL WITH THREE SHAMANIC FIGURES

Sinú
A.D. 100–700
Gold, Weight 90 grams
Height 1¾ in. Width 5³⁄₁₆ in.

This somewhat roughly cast bar pectoral joins at the headdress-level three half-figures whose torsos terminate in a bifurcated shape. The braceleted arms are held outward and the four-fingered hands are open-palmed. The two-tiered headdresses end in points at either side. Projecting, integrally-cast loops hold disk-form danglers which move in front of the faces. Two of the six disks are now missing. The overall condition is good, with varying age patination.

The lot is sold with a statement of authenticity from the distinguished expert Robert Sonin.

Provenance
David Bernstein, New York

Estimate: $8,000-$12,000

47135

HEART-SHAPED PECTORAL

Sinú
A.D. 400–1000
Gold, Weight 98 grams
Height 5¼ in. Width 6⁷⁄₁₆ in.

This large, carefully finished pectoral is worked in a thick gold sheet which gives it substantial weight. This elegant shape is edged with a band of repoussé beading and has two bosses within beaded circles slightly above center. The pectoral retains considerable reddish patina. It is in excellent condition.

The lot is sold with a statement of authenticity from the distinguished expert Robert Sonin.

Provenance
David Bernstein, New York

Estimate: $8,000-$12,000

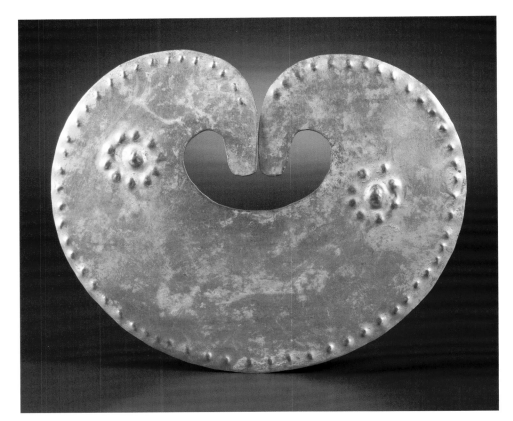

47136

HEART-SHAPED PECTORAL

Sinú
A.D. 400–1000
Gold, Weight 118 grams
Height 5⅛ in. Width 6¼ in.

This large, carefully finished, elegant pectoral is worked in a thick gold sheet giving it substantial weight. The surface is flat with no decoration. The condition is excellent.

The lot is sold with a statement of authenticity from the distinguished expert Robert Sonin.

Provenance
David Bernstein, New York

Estimate: $8,000-$10,000

47137

CIRCULAR PECTORAL

Sinú
A.D. 400–1000
Gold, Weight 108 grams
Maximum Diameter 6¼ in.

This large disk-form pectoral has four raised bosses enclosed by an almost-continuous raised band which forms a clover-leaf shape. A double row of repoussé beading circles the perimeter. Three small stain spots are visible on the front, with the overall condition very good. Two closely-spaced attachment holes are punched at center just above the raised band.

The lot is sold with a statement of authenticity from the distinguished expert Robert Sonin.

Provenance
David Bernstein, New York

Estimate: $8,000-$12,000

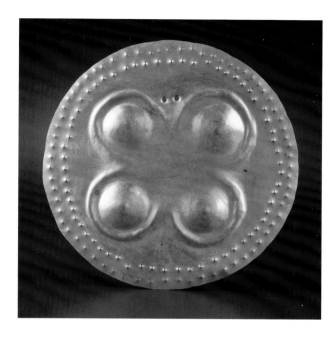

47138

CIRCULAR PECTORAL

Calima
A.D. 400–1000
Gold, Weight 64 grams
Diameter 6¾ in.

The center portion of the pectoral is slightly convex within a double-band border. The inner band is lightly chased with faintly visible circles, while the outer is formed by a double row of repoussé beading. There is one minor edge crack, with overall surface patination. Four evenly distributed holes have been punched for attachment. This high carat example is large and in excellent condition.

Provenance
Christies, Paris: sale 5068, 10 December 2003, p.136, lot 456

Estimate: $6,000-$8,000

47139

CIRCULAR DISK WITH TWO LIZARDS

Quimbaya
A.D. 400–1000
Gold, Weight 16 grams
Diameter 3½ in.

Two vertically-oriented repoussé lizards fill much of the disk. Feet and eyes are carefully detailed, and a row of minute bead shapes follows the spines. Above the pointed noses suspension holes have been punched, and above these double horizontal bands lie below a row of beading. At either side arrow shapes meet the widest part of the lizard bodies. These are formed of three bands bordered inside and outside with beading. A half-inch crack is just to the center of the proper left lizard's tail, and there are small cracks at the snout tip and mid-tail of the proper right lizard as well as a barely visible crack running up its tail from the lower edge.

Provenance
Bonhams & Butterfields, San Francisco: sale 7546E, 14 June 2004, lot 1014, pp.6-7

Estimate: $1,500-$2,500

47140

HUMAN-HEADED BIRD-FORM PECTORAL
REPRESENTING SHAMANIC TRANSFORMATION

Sinú
A.D. 400–1000
Gold, Weight 287.4 grams
Height 14 cm. Width 13.1 cm.

This most unusual bird-form pectoral is rare in representing a human head in place of a bird's. This image fusion represents the actual moment of shamanic transformation. An aureole of spiraling circles surrounds the head, which has a braided head band and a thin circular ornament suspended from his nose. Two spirals at the neck are atop a finely braided band. A double braided band separates profile crested bird heads at the point where the tail begins its outward flaring. The outer two of three large spirals atop the head were cut slightly above their centers and planished smooth at the outer edge. There is a soft age patination, with the overall condition very good.

The lot is sold with a statement of authenticity from the distinguished expert Robert Sonin.

Provenance
David Bernstein, New York

Estimate: $25,000-$30,000

47141

BIRD-FORM PECTORAL

Sinú
A.D. 400–1000
Gold, Weight 90 grams
Height 3⅝ in. Width 4¾ in.

The hammered components of the pectoral form a widely flared tail and wings which curve downward with a strongly circular force. The cast body and head are globular and full, with a large, downward-curving beak. The small, bead-like eyes are widely set. A delicate braided necklace is balanced by braids below the body that terminate in outward-facing birds' heads. The reddish age patination is relatively untouched, and there are several small casting losses in head and beak.

The lot is sold with a statement of authenticity from the distinguished expert Robert Sonin.

Provenance
David Bernstein, New York

Estimate: $8,000-$12,000

47142

ANIMAL-FORM PENDANT WITH HUMAN HEAD

Quimbaya
A.D. 400–1000
Gold, Weight 92 grams
Height 2⅛ in. Length 2¹¹⁄₁₆ in.

This pendant shows an animal with raised tail of the configuration prevalent among pieces of the so-called International Style. It is unusual in having a human head which faces to the creature's left. This head is in a style reminiscent of Quimbaya figural pieces. Connected spirals replace ears, and a capped tube at top center of the head suggests a misunderstood *poporo* spout. In generally very good condition, there is a small hole in the proper right of the head, a casting fault.

Provenance
Splendors of the World, Haiku, Hawaii

Estimate: $8,000-$12,000

47143

DOUBLE SPIRAL ORNAMENT FOR CEREMONIAL USE

Tairona
A.D. 1000–1500
Tumbaga, Weight 26 grams
Height 2⅝ in. Width 5¹³/₁₆ in.

Of elegant design, this double spiral ornament has been cut from a sheet of high–grade *tumbaga* and given a slight torque so that the central portion is somewhat convex. The condition is good, with some age patination.

Provenance
Christies, Paris: sale 5057, 12 June 2003, lot 566

Estimate: $1,500-$2,500

47144

MONUMENTAL STANDING FIGURE, POSSIBLY A SHAMAN

Quimbaya, Urabá Area
A.D. 500–1000
Gold, Weight 287.4 grams
Height 6½ in. Width 3⁷⁄₁₆ in.

This statuesque figure represents a standing shaman in trance state. It exhibits the prime Quimbaya sculptural quality of monumental grandeur that belies the actual size (though this is still an exceptionally large and heavy pendant figure). He wears a wing-shaped nose ornament of a type for which many fine examples survive. The fine threads which form the broad necklace, the waist band and other bands, and the paired headdress curls were made by wax melted in a section of cane and forced out by a plunger through a small hole into cold water (Robert Sonin, letter of 17 March 2006). The fingers, unusual in their continuation up the arm, were made with wider gauge threads (a figure with identical finger-arm treatment and flattened, outward-thrust feet is in a 1968 Museo del Oro publication, on the cover and on page 6; that example is smaller and far less sculptural and elegant than the present piece). The progress from wholly developed, highly sculptural three-dimensionality in the head, shoulders, and torso toward the much flatter, conceptualized legs and feet is frequently seen in Quimbaya area figural pieces. Holes cast at each side of the neck indicate that this figure was intended at times to be suspended. The effort by the gold workers to use smaller amounts of gold has resulted in thin spots in the lower body area, with minute openings visible on either leg. Other than minor stains on the lower body, the piece is in excellent condition.

This lot is sold with a statement of authenticity from the distinguished expert Robert Sonin, and a laboratory report from Conservation and Technical Services Limited, London (Dr. A.T. N. Bennett).

Provenance
Sra Garrido's Family (from circa 1900)
Ofelia Garrido, Dunedin, Florida (from the early 1940's)
William Siegal, Santa Fe, New Mexico

Estimate: $120,000-$160,000

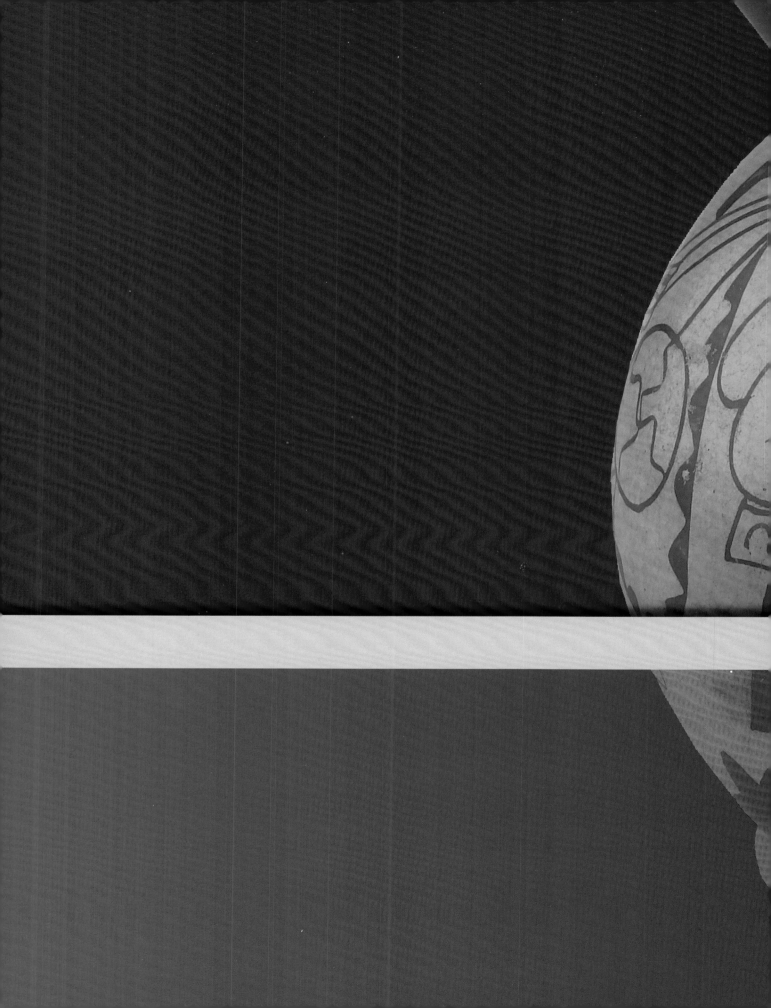

PERU

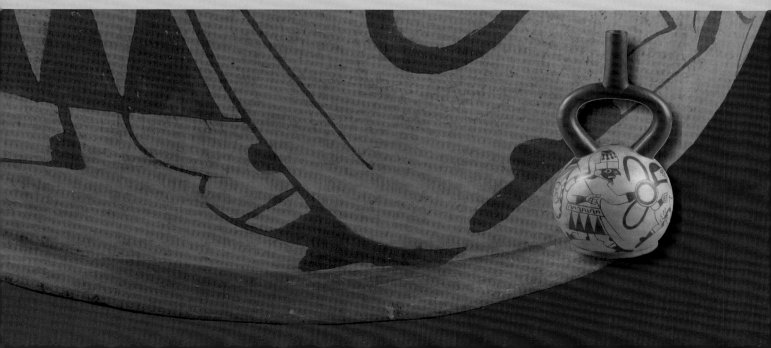

47145

STIRRUP-SPOUT VESSEL WITH FELINE

Chavín, Cupisnique
1000 – 600 B.C.
Burnished and slipped ceramic, red and white pigment
Height 11¼ in. Width 7½ in.

While felines on Cupisnique vessels are most commonly shown in conjunction with the San Pedro cactus, this representation places the cat in a cave-like area in the side of what is assumed to be a gourd grown in a net to give it the shape seen here (Junius Bird, personal communication). These Cupisnique felines are strongly conventionalized as in this example: three-clawed, a few large donut spots, fanged mouth with a peaked lift at center upper lip, and an eyebrow unit that extends in a strong line to the nostrils. Commonly they face directly outward or back toward the raised tail as here. Throughout much of South America, continuing into the present, the principal shamanic alter ego is the large feline. Other than some minor restored breaks, the condition is good.

Provenance
David Bernstein, New York

Estimate: $5,000-$7,000

47146

LOW BOWL WITH INCISED EXTERIOR

Chavín
1000–600 B.C.
Burnished blackware with red pigment
Height 1¾ in. Diameter 7⅝ in.

The deeply-incised exterior of this burnished blackware bowl is divided by double bands into four balanced fields, two larger and two smaller. The abutting dynamic, arrow-like large fields occupy the majority of the bottom and two outwardly sloped vessel sides. A complex profile monster occupies all four compartments, the two larger examples more fully developed and more easily readable. Head directions of the monsters alternate across the vessel, in each case at the broader end of the triangular compartment. The larger monster's head is comprised of squared-off elements, and includes prominent everted lips and a rectangular eye. Squared scrolls emanate from the mouth. Its smaller-sized body is formed of a highly conventionalized, downward-facing profile head with down-turned mouth and a forehead curl which also can be read as the tail of the profile monster. The smaller compartments read first as an angularly-stylized profile head facing toward the vessel's center, but the general

configuration, eye placement, and a large curling shape below the head together strongly evoke a zoomorph seen in profile. This smaller head-form has a toothed, downturned mouth and squared eyes. The deeply-cut incising has resulted in broad sunken areas; these are filled with vermillion pigment. There are restored breaks, but all parts are original.

Provenance
David Bernstein, New York

Estimate: $4,000-$5,000

47147

STIRRUP-SPOUT VESSEL

Chavín, Tembladera
1000–600 B.C.
Carved and burnished brownware
Height 9¾ in. Diameter 4⅝ in.

The complex, densely-packed imagery of this exceptional vessel indicates that it was connected with the core of the Chavín belief system. Such vessels, along with equally portable painted textiles, were the primary means through which the Chavín cult was propagated across extensive geographic areas from the highland center of its development and elaboration, Chavín de Huántar. The dynamic carving of this vessel is integrally employed to signal the principal motif, a fanged avian raptor. Six pairs of fangs project sharply outward from the six appearances of this creature's head, two on the upper main vessel body, one on either side of the stirrup, and two on the short vertical spout. These fangs spatially differentiate the primary heads from two more large, differently-configured heads on the lower vessel body. Two carved wings are so situated that they are shared by all four large heads on the main vessel body. Such multiple interactions provide visual equivalents for the reiterative structure of most ritual texts. The overall condition is very good, with parts of three projecting fangs missing and minor chipping at the spout lip.

Provenance
David Bernstein, New York

Estimate: $13,000-$15,000

47148

STIRRUP-SPOUT VESSEL

Chavín, Cupisnique
1000–600 B.C.
Burnished and textured blackware
Height 9¼ in. Diameter 5¾ in.

Burnished tendril-like forms in raised relief create an assertive surface activity on this classic example of Chavín stirrup-spout vessel shape. The background surface textured with long parallel incised lines adds a stronger visual three-dimensionality. The unbroken vessel is in good condition, with minor chipping and surface losses on the spout.

Provenance
David Bernstein, New York

Estimate: $4,500-$5,500

47149

SINGLE-SPOUT BOTTLE

Chavín, Tembladera
1000–600 B.C.
Burnished and textured blackware
Height 9½ in. Diameter 5¾ in.

This vessel, which represents one standard Chavín ceramic shape, embodies the extraordinary technical perfection and elegance characteristic of this early culture. A further indication of Chavín sophistication is the way in which the textures of vessel surfaces are developed organically in harmony with shape to create a much more complex set of visual rhythms than might seem possible from the relatively few basic elements. The interaction of matte texture with reflective burnished areas adds a further level of visual activity. Overall condition is good, with minor patches near lip of spout, small areas of loss in the textured area of one spiral, and a few surface scratches.

Provenance
David Bernstein, New York

Estimate: $2,500-$3,500

47150

STIRRUP-SPOUT VESSEL

Chavín, Cupisnique
1000–600 B.C.
Burnished blackware
Height 9½in. Width 8¹¹⁄₁₆ in.

A complex plant form (possibly an *achira [Canna edulis]*) is represented in this stirrup-spout vessel, in which some details are modeled in full-round and some are hastily engraved after firing. Representations of plants important to ancient Peruvian societies appear as subjects of finely made stirrup-spout vessels from Chavín times on through the rest of north and central coast pre-Spanish history. Such continuity and prominence, along with the known status and ritual importance of the stirrup-spout type, indicate the continuing important place of plant representation in ritual and social contexts. The condition is good, with some minor crack restoration. Drill holes in the bottom indicate that clay samples were taken.

Provenance
David Bernstein, New York

Estimate: $4,000-$5,000

47151

STIRRUP-SPOUT VESSEL: FANGED DEITY

Chavín
700–400 B.C.
Burnished dark gray ceramic
Height 8½ in. Width 5½ in.

This vessel exemplifies one Chavín-related mode of decoration: finely burnished dark gray surfaces are combined with matte textured areas and incised linear patterning. The full-formed vessel incorporates the frontal face of a fanged deity with wrinkled forehead, the latter along with the nose and ears shown in low relief. The full, short-spouted stirrup typical of Cupisnique-type vessels is seen here. The overall condition is good, with minor surface losses, and drilled indications that two clay samples were taken.

Provenance
Bonhams & Butterfields, San Francisco: sale 7477E, 8 December 2003, Lot 3035 (p.15, ill., p.14)

Estimate: $2,000-$2,500

47152

STIRRUP-SPOUT VESSEL: HEAD OF A MYTHICAL CREATURE

Chavinoid
600–400 B.C.
Burnished gray ware, red pigment
Height 9 in.

The unusual and somewhat puzzling iconography of this vessel suggests that it is either provincial in origin or very late in the Chavín-influenced sequence. The burnished areas of the vessel body are filled with a boldly-incised fanged head with large three-part eyes below striations possibly intended as eye lashes. A cap-like head-covering, divided down the center, ends in two outward-projecting points. The rest of the head area is lightly textured. The vessel settled during firing, which causes it to rest crookedly. The entire body of the vessel has been rubbed with red pigment. Overall condition is good, with minor pitting on the vertical spout and a clay sample drill hole in the base.

Provenance
Bonhams & Butterfields, San Francisco: sale 7477E, 8 December 2003, Lot 3034 (p.15, ill., p.14)

Estimate: $2,500-$3,000

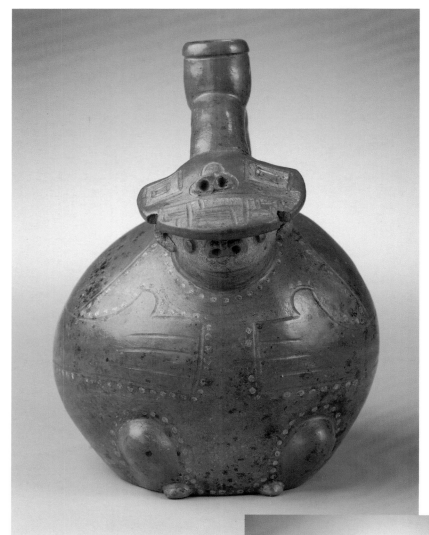

47153

STIRRUP-SPOUT VESSEL

Chavín, Tembladera
1000–600 B.C.
Burnished ceramic
Height 8⁷⁄₈ in. Width 6½ in.

This unusual vessel in two tones of burnished orange-red slips shows a seated figure whose head is overshadowed by a monstrous mask intended to be viewed from above. The head, lower legs, and feet of the figure are developed three-dimensionally, while the greatly exaggerated arms and hands are incised into the globular body of the vessel. Evenly-spaced white slip spots outline arms and hands and form a necklace. A similar spotted band lies along the legs and just above the lower edge of the vessel. The figure's face is as much simian as human, with small round eyes and snub nose. The mask that forms the hat-like headdress has a fully three-dimensional human nose, incised square eyes, and incised rectangular mouth with interlocking fangs. An artful distribution of slip colors enhances the definition of different shapes throughout. The condition is good with some repair of cracks.

Provenance
Butterfields, San Francisco: sale 7305A, 25 March 2002, lot 5099, p.29
David Bernstein, New York

Estimate: $4,500-$5,500

47154

STIRRUP-SPOUT PORTRAIT VESSEL

Salinar (?)
300–100 B.C.
Ceramic with dark brown paint
Height 8¼ in. Width 5¾ in.

Several features of this vessel are unusual, starting with the style of the image itself, which is closest to the facial type found on Salinar ceramics. That combined with the lipped stirrup–spout form suggests a relatively early date. Surface dents at the upper back, a slight torque and dent to the spout, and a surface almost granular in places all indicate that the firing of the vessel went awry. Even with these anomalies the strong rendering of the face combines with the striking facial painting to create an arresting image.

Provenance
Arte Textil (Steve Berger), San Francisco, California

Estimate: $2,000-$2,500

47155

DOUBLE-CHAMBERED SINGLE-SPOUT VESSEL

Salinar
300–100 B.C.
Burnished orangeware, resist painting
Height 7⅝ in. Width 3¾ in.

The squared-off front chamber is topped by an open-fronted shrine inside which can be seen a large head. Two smaller heads flank the flat area in front of the shrine. The total unit indicates one form of shrine developed by the Salinar culture. The globular rear chamber rests on a low-flanged base and contains the slightly backward-slanting spout. The overall condition is good, with some reglued breaks and minor fills. Missing parts of the flanged base have been replaced.

Provenance
Bonhams & Butterfields, San Francisco: sale 7437 E, 9 June 2003, lot 5076, pp.18-19

Estimate: $2,000-$3,000

47156

HALF STIRRUP-SPOUT VESSEL WITH TWIN-PEAKED BUILDING

Moche
A.D. 300–600
Burnished orangeware, with red slip
Height 9 in. Diameter 5¾ in.

A simple rectangular structure is set atop the globular vessel, its roof stepped upward to peaks at either end. A red slip was used to pick up roof details, as well as showing what are probably two covered jars set near the building. A fanned arrangement of disk shapes at the end of cords is painted on the back surface under the arch of the spout. Small holes in the vessel body have been repaired and there is some surface chipping.

Provenance
Bonhams & Butterfields, San Francisco: sale 7437E, 9 June 2003, lot 5075, pp.18–19

Estimate: $700-$1,000

47157

STIRRUP-SPOUT VESSEL WITH CIRCULAR PYRAMID TOPPED BY A RECTANGULAR BUILDING

Moche
A.D. 300–600
Burnished Brownware with red slip
Height 7 in. Width 4⅝ in.

A three-level circular pyramid is set on a low flanged base. A rectangular building rests on top with its roof stepping outward and upward toward either end. A blade of the same form as those seen on headdresses of Moche warriors rises from the center of the roof to a level slightly higher than the end peaks. Along the top tier of the pyramid a serpent-like form originates at the proper left base of the spout, from which it passes along the side of the tier to the front center, where it flows up and into the central door of the building. A small segment of similar shape at the proper left rear of the roof passes from under the headdress element to the upper spout base, suggesting that this tubular element, whatever it may represent, forms a continuous loop. While overall condition is good, the top half of the spout and the center of the roof blade are replacements.

Provenance
Bonhams & Butterfields, San Francisco: sale 7437E, 9 June 2003, pp.18–19, lot 5075

Estimate: $1,000-$1,200

47158

STIRRUP-SPOUT VESSEL WITH SACRIFICIAL SCENE

Moche
A.D. 300–600
Polychrome ceramic
Height 7⅛ in. Width 4¼ in.

A stepped, rectangular structure forms the setting of a scene in which a fanged deity seated on a platform at top center receives prisoners. Iguana warriors stand at top and bottom of a ramp holding a rope that joins four captive birds shown ascending the ramp. The lower warrior wears a headdress topped by a similar bird and holds a large dart in his left hand, while the upper warrior holds a bundle of darts. All the participants are rendered in low relief on the surface. Freely brushed cream-colored linear patterns cover the light brown structure. The overall condition is good, with minor flaking on the stirrup and several relief images are slightly abraded.

Provenance
Bonhams & Butterfields, San Francisco: sale 7437E, 9 June 2003, lot 5074, pp.17-18

Estimate: $1,000-$1,500

47159

STIRRUP-SPOUT PORTRAIT VESSEL

Moche
A.D. 300–600
Polychrome ceramic
Height 11½ in. Width 6 in.

This solemn-looking individual wears one type of headdress seen on stirrup-spout portraits, in which a patterned headband is punctuated to the right of center by a projection in the shape of a warclub head. Strands of hair frame the face, with tubular ear ornaments just outside these. Painted pupils in the eyes animate the face. Even though mold-made, the definition of features is sharp. The lower area of the vessel is rebuilt, and overall there is repainting to strengthen color areas.

Provenance
Skinner, Boston: sale 2209, 20 September 2003, lot 70, p.21

Estimate: $4,000-$6,000

47160

PORTRAIT VESSEL

Moche
A.D. 300–600
Ceramic
Height 7 in. Width 5½ in.

The turban-like head covering secured with a cloth band under the chin is one frequently seen in Moche mode of dress. Strands of the hair show below the chinstrap at either side. The shape of this vessel indicates that it may have been used as a cup. The overall condition is good, with a minor rim chip at back and light abrasion on the tip of the nose.

Provenance
Bonhams & Butterfields, San Francisco: sale 7477E, 8 December 2003, lot 3058, pp.18-19

Estimate: $1,800-$2,400

47161

STIRRUP-SPOUT VESSEL: SEATED FIGURE

Moche (Early)
100 B.C.–A.D. 200
Burnished blackware
Height 6¼ in. Width 4⅞ in.

This alert–looking seated figure with carefully defined hands resting on its knees evidences the energetic, highly finished carving characteristic of Early Moche ceramics. A subtly distended left cheek indicates that the subject is engaged in chewing coca. Inlaid elements are another early component (in this example the eye inlays are new replacements). Altogether the vessel became a convincing stand–in for an actual individual, thus early establishing the qualities of insightful realism for which Moche art is known. Condition is good, with minor surface restorations.

Provenance
David Bernstein, New York

Estimate: $4,000-$5,000

47162

PAIR OF FIGURAL EFFIGY JARS

Moche (Loma Negra?)
200 B.C.–A.D. 100
Ceramic, burnished blackware
(A) Height 9 in. Width 5 in.
(B) Height 9 in. Width 5 in.

The virtually identical vessels show standing warriors, each with a small round war shield hiding the right hand and the left hand holding a war club diagonally across the chest. They wear a simple band headdress with arc shapes over each eye, simple loincloths, crescent-shaped nose ornaments, and tubular earspools. The principal piece of clothing is a sleeveless tunic divided into squares. Integral with the back of the tunic is a displayed figure with grimacing face, the head and arms and legs shown in relief. This may be an emblem in metal repoussé of the kind found in the Loma Negra area. Both vessels have minor chipping, and one has a repaired area at the back.

Provenance
Bonhams & Butterfields, San Francisco: sale 7437E, 9 June 2003, lot 5094, p.22

Estimate: $3,000-$4,000

47163

STIRRUP-SPOUT VESSEL: SEATED FIGURE

Moche
A.D. 300–600
Burnished buff ceramic and slip
Height 7⅜ in. Width 6½ in.

The cross-legged seated figure is bent slightly forward, the hands hanging loosely over the calves. Though heavily robed, with a head covering tied below the chin, circular earspools are still visible. The tellingly rendered face has a profoundly distressed expression. The mouth and chin area, as well as the hands are painted with a dark brown slip, which also picks up a few simple details of clothing. Other than minor chips at the lip of the spout the overall condition is good.

Provenance
Bonhams & Butterfields, San Francisco: sale 7477E, 8 December 2003, lot 3051, pp. 17-18

Estimate: $600-$900

47164

STIRRUP-SPOUT VESSEL: SEATED FIGURE

Moche
A.D. 200–500
Burnished ceramic
Height 7 in. Width 4⅞ in.

The deftly simplified but still lively figure is seated cross-legged, the right leg and foot visible along the vessel front. The hands rest on the knees. The head is covered by a simple cloth, and large slightly-flared tubular earspools frame the cheeks. Attention focuses on the expressive face, with its prominent nose and jaw area. Facial ornament has been delicately incised at the temples, down the nose, and across the chin between the ear ornaments. An incised triangle at the center lower lip, apex upward, completes the incised facial decoration. Slip application with subtle color variation further defines the modeled lips, eyes, and hair areas. The condition is good, with a small pressure crack near the proper right rear base. The vessel may have been waxed.

Provenance
Bonhams & Butterfields, San Francisco: sale 7477E, 8 December 2003, pp.17-18, lot 3051

Estimate: $600-$900

47165

PORTRAIT VESSEL

Moche
A.D. 250–500
Ceramic, white slip
Height 9¾ in. Width 10¼ in.

This portrait vessel exemplifies the best qualities of mature Moche ceramic development, in which mold-made components are combined and given individual finishing refinements that result in a lively entity. This assertive-looking individual, whose portrait occurs on other vessels, is wearing a headdress made from an entire feline pelt, as indicated by the spotted encircling band and the simplified tail and leg-like appendages on the back of the head. The animal's expression and exaggeratedly large flared claws produce an aggressive look. Large circular ear ornaments complete the accoutrements of this large-sized portrait. Condition is very good.

Provenance
David Bernstein, New York

Estimate: $6,000-$7,000

47166

STIRRUP-SPOUT PORTRAIT VESSEL

Moche
A.D. 300–600
Burnished and slipped ceramic
Height 11¼ in. Width 6⅞ in.

The vessel shows a full-faced male wearing disk earrings, the stirrup-spout oriented in line with his nose. The front base of the spout issues from a clipped shock of hair above the central forehead. An expression of self-assurance animates the portrait. Such vessels were made from molds in considerable numbers. Since images of the same person have been found in varying contexts, it is thought that the portrait vessels were important in Moche socio-political exchanges. The overall condition is good, with minor abrasions and chipping at the rim of the spout. Both ears have been repaired and infilled.

Provenance
Bonhams & Butterfields, San Francisco: sale 7437E, 9 June 2003, lot 5091, pp.21, 22

Estimate: $2,000-$2,500

47167

STIRRUP-SPOUT VESSEL WITH EAGLE WARRIOR

Moche (late)
A.D. 450–600
Ceramic with red and cream slip
Height 11½ in. Width 5⅞ in.

The red and cream slip colors divide the vessel body perpendicularly to the main axis of the stirrup, with the red and cream distribution reversing on the stirrup spout itself. A profile eagle warrior in red fine-line painting is shown in an active pose against the cream ground. The composite warrior has a large-eyed eagle head with a three-point crest, one human arm and leg, and a bird's wing and tail. The human arm supports a round war shield behind which is an arrangement of fanned darts centered by a war club. The shape of the stirrup spout indicates a late position in the Moche sequence. There are minor chips on the spout rim along with minor surface pitting and scratches.

Provenance
Bonhams & Butterfields, San Francisco: sale 7437E, 9 June 2003, lot 5093, p.22

Estimate: $3,000-$5,000

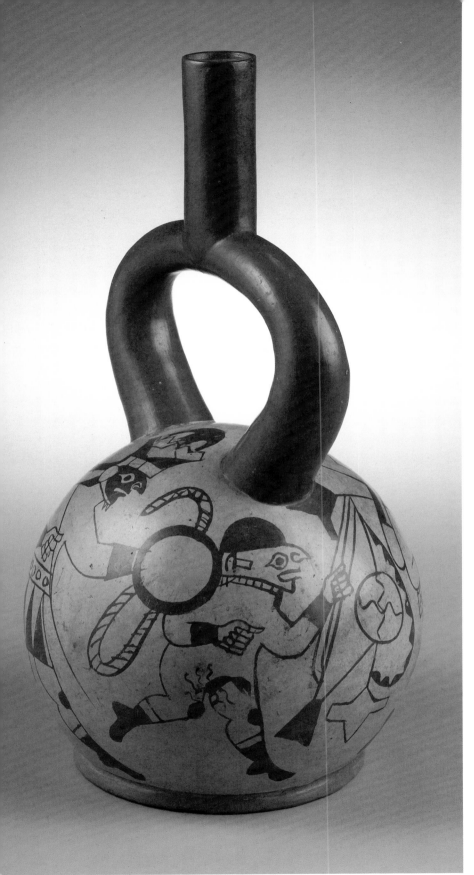

47168

STIRRUP-SPOUT VESSEL WITH WARRIORS AND PRISONERS

Moche
A.D. 300–600
Ceramic, red on buff
Height 11¼ in. Diameter 6¾ in.

Two pairs of figures in fine-line painting are shown in rapid motion around this elegant fourth-stage stirrup-spout vessel. In both pairs a naked prisoner runs before an armed warrior who reins in the prisoner by a neck cord held in the left hand along with a small round war shield. Each warrior holds in his right hand a weapon with a club head on a wire-thin shaft. The warriors wear differing helmets and waist bands but similar kilts. Each prisoner carries in his left hand a "trophy" of his own stripped arms. In Moche society nakedness constituted an extreme form of humiliation of captives. The vessel is in good overall condition, with two small drill pits in the base, although the owner's records did not include laboratory reports.

Provenance
Sotheby's, New York: sale 7902, 15 May 2003, lot 270, pp.182–183

Estimate: $4,000-$6,000

47169

HEADDRESS FRONTAL ORNAMENT WITH FELINE HEAD

Moche (Early)
100 B.C.–A.D. 200
Gold, turquoise or chrysacola, Weight 106 grams
Height 7½ in. Width 13 in.

Parallel crescent-shaped bands arc outward from the central base to establish the overall configuration of this ornament, which formed the central frontal element of a high status headdress for a secular or religious leader. Near each end these bands are stabilized by a smaller arced strip moving perpendicularly to the sweep of the main strips. Small circular danglers are attached along both edges of both strips. When worn these would have created a brilliantly shimmering screen of light above the wearer's head. The central ornament base has an attached repoussé feline head. It is flanked by two loops to which were attached dangling blue-green paws (either turquoise or chrysacola), the proper right of which remains. Where the whiskers of the feline head would have grown, the proper right retains a projecting gold wire with a triangular dangle. A remaining hole indicates that there was one at the left as well. Four slots for attachment to the headdress were cut on the broad basal tab. Five of the circular dangles are now missing. Other than minor cracking in the feline head and light surface staining, the condition is very good.

This lot is sold with a technical report from Orenda Investigation and Analysis of Artifacts and Antiquities, Santa Fe (Frank Aon).

Provenance
Collection of Eugenia Alvarez
Katalin Horvath, Budapest
David Bernstein Fine Art, New York (1975-2002)

Estimate: $12,000-$18,000

47170

CEREMONIAL TWEEZERS WITH A CENTRAL HUMAN HEAD

Moche (early)
200 B.C.–A.D. 100
Gold; turquoise (?); traces of red pigment, Weight 58 grams
Height 4⅜ in. Width 8⅛ in.

Outward-facing bird heads terminate the large arced crescent of the tweezers. A staring frontal head forms a focal point above the center of the arc, with a suspension loop at top center. The eyes of both frontal head and bird heads are inlaid with turquoise-colored beads. Circular ornaments dangle from each ear. Such large tweezers in gold must have transcended their utilitarian origins and have become designators of power and prestige. While the overall condition is good, the head of the proper left bird is damaged, with the stone missing from the eyes and the central head is separating at its left. There is minor edge denting overall.

Provenance
Splendors of the World, Haiku, Hawaii

Estimate: $8,000-$12,000

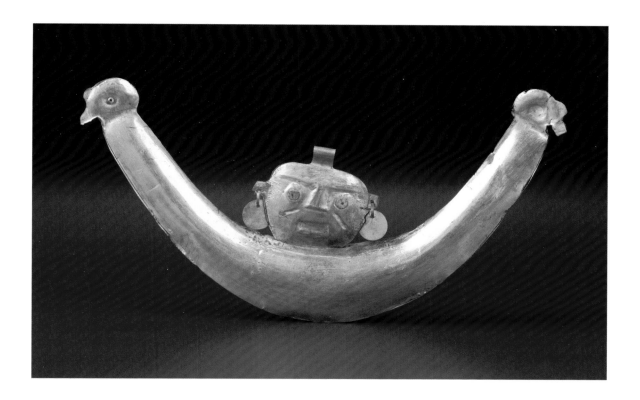

47171

CROWN WITH DANGLES

Moche (?)
A.D. 100–500
Gold
Height 6⅜ in. Diameter 7½ in.

A crown of such unadorned design is very difficult to place culturally when the provenance is lacking. This example is formed of a plain gold primary crown form, to which elegant, spiral-decorated danglers have been attached at the top and along the lower rim. The condition is generally good, but a few danglers are missing. There are many complex ancient stains, one area suggesting contact with a necklace with rectangular pendant components. On the front half multiple disk-shaped impressions of clear gold are surrounded by a cloudy field with some corroded cloth evidence. Thus the crown gives at least ghostly hints of the elaborate, perhaps royal costuming of which it was once a part.

Provenance
Bonhams & Butterfields, San Francisco: sale 7437E, 9 June 2003, lot 5105, pp.24-25

Published
Jose Antonio de Lavalle, Editor, *Oro del Antiguo Peru,* Banco del Credito del Peru, Lima, 1972, p.106, ill.93

Estimate: $15,000-$20,000

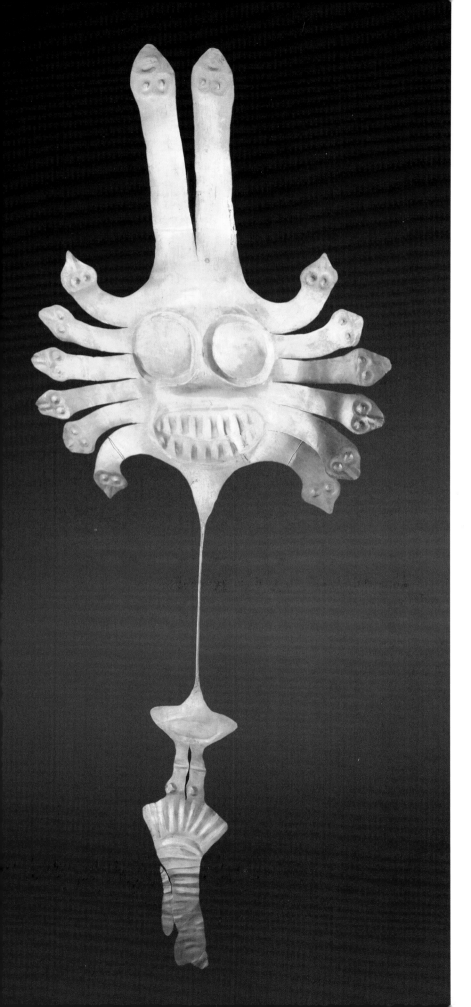

47172

SHAMAN'S CEREMONIAL DANCE WAND

Nasca
100 B.C.–A.D. 400
Gold, Weight 54 grams
Height 16⅜ in. Width 6⁹⁄₁₆ in.

This unusually large long-handled ceremonial dance wand topped with a round-eyed, well-toothed and large-mouthed slightly smiling face was used during trance-related dance ceremonies. Two large, serpent-headed elements project upward from the center of the forehead. Six serpent-headed hair units curl outward on either side of the face. A delicate, pointed chin develops downward into an unusually thin handle at the lower terminus of which swells a complex low relief unit replicating a handle. Other than losses at the lower end, which from their edges appear to be ancient, some smoothed fold creases are visible.

Provenance
Lawrence Witten Collection
David Bernstein, New York

Estimate: $18,000-$24,000

47173

PAIR OF CEREMONIAL VESSELS

Moche (Early)
100 B.C.–A.D. 200
Gold, Weight 118 grams
(A) Height 1⅝ in. Diameter 4⅝ in.
(B) Height 1⅝ in. Diameter 4⅝ in.

This pair of ceremonial bowls is identical in size. Each has a center dimple thrusting upward into the interior, from which swirled bands fan upward, enlarging in width as the contours increase. These terminate at a top bordering band which is punctuated by a series of circles with raised bosses in their centers. Both bowls are in good condition with minor surface stains, and one has two small scratches.

Provenance
Splendors of the World, Haiku, Hawaii

Estimate: $12,000-$18,000

47174

TWO CEREMONIAL BOWLS

Moche (Early)
100 B.C.–A.D. 200
Gold, Weight 148 grams
(A) Height 2⅝ in. Width 4⅜ in.
(B) Height 2⁹⁄₁₆ in. Width 4 in.

While the two bowls probably began as identical, at some point the rim of one was crimped on opposite sides to produce a rim shape much like a wide-open eye. Both bowls have a broad band of raised chevron pattern covering all of the side except for a small plain band at top. The condition of both is excellent, with minor surface stains.

Provenance
Splendors of the World, Haiku, Hawaii

Estimate: $8,000-$12,000

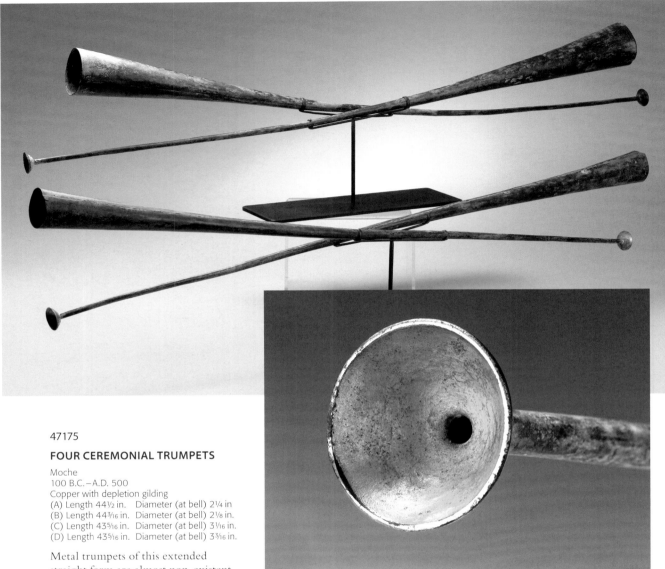

47175

FOUR CEREMONIAL TRUMPETS

Moche
100 B.C.–A.D. 500
Copper with depletion gilding
(A) Length 44½ in. Diameter (at bell) 2¼ in
(B) Length 44³⁄₁₆ in. Diameter (at bell) 2⅛ in.
(C) Length 43⁵⁄₁₆ in. Diameter (at bell) 3¹⁄₁₆ in.
(D) Length 43⁵⁄₁₆ in. Diameter (at bell) 3³⁄₁₆ in.

Metal trumpets of this extended straight form are almost non-existent in the literature. One set, also of four essentially identical gilded examples, is in the private Peruvian collection of Enrico Poli Bianchi (Duccio Bonavia. *Arte e Historia del Peru Antiguo. Colección Enrico Poli Bianchi.* Arequipa, Peru: Banco del Sur, 1994. p.177, pl. 140; no cultural or chronological attribution is given, but they are localized at Pacatnamú). The fact that the present set is also of four closely matched trumpets raises the interesting question whether this was the usual number, and that there was some cosmological significance connected with their ceremonial use. Although these four trumpets are similar in overall size, configuration, and structural method, each trumpet has individual qualities. Bell diameters vary slightly, and there are differences in the use of tabs near the bell to stabilize the overlapped jointure of the sheet copper. More remaining depletion gilding survives on the cupped mouthpieces than elsewhere. The general condition is good, with light surface corrosion and a few small cracks.

Provenance
Splendors of the World, Haiku, Hawaii

Estimate: $25,000-$35,000

47176

HEADBAND

Moche
A.D. 100 – 500
Gold
Height 1⅝ in. Diameter 6¼ in.

A plain gold band, possibly used as a crown, has been retied to form a head-sized circlet. It has one arc-shaped, stabilized crack, as well as some surface stains. Otherwise, the condition is good.

Provenance
Splendors of the World, Haiku, Hawaii

Estimate: $6,000-$8,000

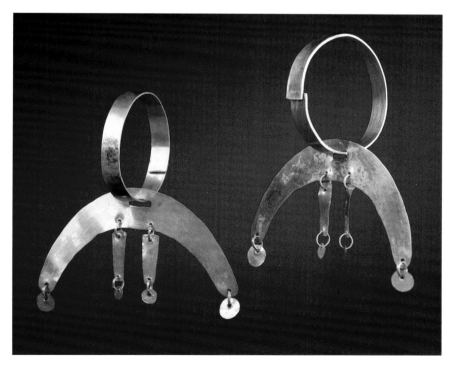

47177

PAIR OF EAR ORNAMENTS

Moche
A.D. 100 – 500
Gold, Weight 66 grams
Earloop Diameters 2 – 2⅛ in.
Crescent Dangler Heights 2 – 2¼ in. Widths 3¾ in.

The earloops are of a heavier gauge gold than that of the downward-turned crescents which hang from them. These crescents are punched at lower center and ends for attached danglers, the outer two circular. The center two danglers are greatly elongated ovals with holes in their lower ends from which hang small circular danglers. Other than some stains and a minor age crack in one crescent, the condition is very good.

Provenance
Splendors of the World, Haiku, Hawaii

Estimate: $2,000-$3,000

47178

MONUMENTAL CROWN-SHAPED EMBLEM WITH "DECAPITATOR" DEITY

Moche (early)
100 B.C.–A.D. 300
Gold, Weight 1200 grams
Height 23⅜ in. Width 31⅝ in.

This exceptionally large crescent-shaped emblem is in the shape of crowns or helmets worn by important Moche warriors. A bottom center tab with three punched holes indicates that it was part of an assembly of several components. The lower central portion is filled by the image of the "Decapitator" (Rebecca Stone-Miller. *Art of the Andes from Chavín to Inca.* New York: Thames and Hudson, 1995, p.98), framed by a band replicating in low relief circular dangling elements. The fanged deity, in an aggressive frontal pose, stands in front of doubled diagonally-crossed bands. In his right hand he holds a knife with a carrying loop, and in his left, a profile human trophy head grasped by its long hair. In the center of the deity's curled headdress is a small frontal head, and he wears a necklace of owl heads.

The impressive scale raises the interesting possibility that this piece was made for use in a large temple or on a shrine effigy. The decisive execution of the repoussé work which creates the image is indicative of the hand of a master artist. In addition to surface stains, a number of cracks inward from the edges have been stabilized and repaired.

Provenance
Dr. Kurt Zalud, Lima (pre-1960's)
Heintz Kaelin collection, Zurich
Margarit Brenner, Zurich, 1980-1989
Michael Bernstein, Tucson, Arizona

Estimate: $40,000-$60,000

47179

**SMALL BOWL WITH SIX
REPOUSSÉ LIZARDS**

Moche (early)
A.D. 100–300
Gold, Weight 26 grams
Height 1½ in. Diameter 3 in.

This low, rather shallow bowl is in
good quality gold, as can be seen
by the smooth finish the rim takes.
Six repoussé lizards, shown as seen
from above, face upward toward the
rim, as though they are emerging
from beneath the bowl. Their shapes
are conventionalized in a strongly
linear way well suited to the repoussé
technique, with elements such as toes
and heads strongly geometricized.
The condition is good, with some
light surface staining.

Provenance
Splendors of the World, Haiku, Hawaii

Estimate: $2,000-$3,000

47180

PAIR OF LOW CEREMONIAL BOWLS

Moche
A.D. 100–600
Gold, Weight 182 grams
Height 1⅞ in. Diameter 5 in.

This closely matched pair of low bowls is raised from a thick gold sheet, giving them unusual weight for their size. On each, seven radically simplified profile zoomorphs process in single file just below the upper rim. These stand out in sharp relief on the outer surface due to the pressure of the chasing used to delineate them. Both vessels are in generally good condition, but both have light surface staining and small cracks.

Provenance
Splendors of the World, Haiku, Hawaii

Estimate: $12,000-$15,000

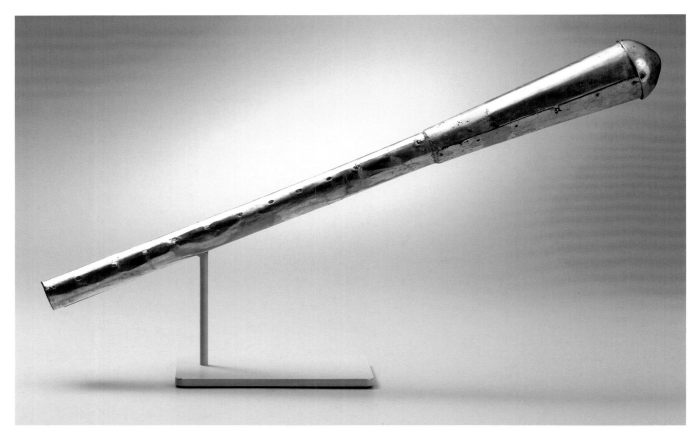

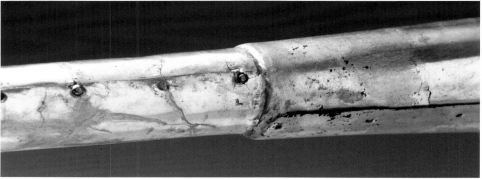

47181

CEREMONIAL WAR CLUB

Moche
100 B.C.- A.D. 500
Gold sheathing over (?) wood
Length 20⅜ in. Diameter 2¹/₁₆ in.

The ceremonial designation is used in describing these Moche outward-tapering clubs with domed weapon ends because of the complete sheathing with a rather good quality of gold. Separate sheets of gold were wrapped around both the smaller-diameter lower end and the swelling upper, with another piece of sheeting used to sheathe the domed end. What are possibly a few remaining original attaching brads are rectangular in cross-section and appear to be made of copper. Most of the brads are modern replacements. There is some cracking and loss at several brad jointures, and there are signs of recent removal of surface corrosion in a few areas. The condition is otherwise very good.

Provenance
Splendors of the World, Haiku, Hawaii

Estimate: $8,000-$12,000

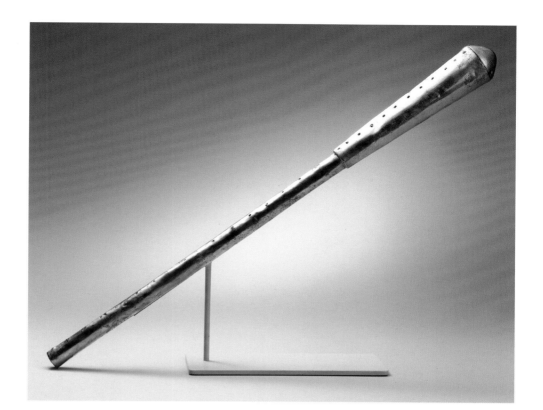

47182

CEREMONIAL WAR CLUB

Moche
100 B.C.–A.D. 500
Gold sheathing over (?) wood
Length 29⁹⁄₁₆ in. Diameter 2⁹⁄₁₆ in.

See description in Lot 47181.

Provenance
Splendors of the World, Haiku, Hawaii

Estimate: $12,000-$14,000

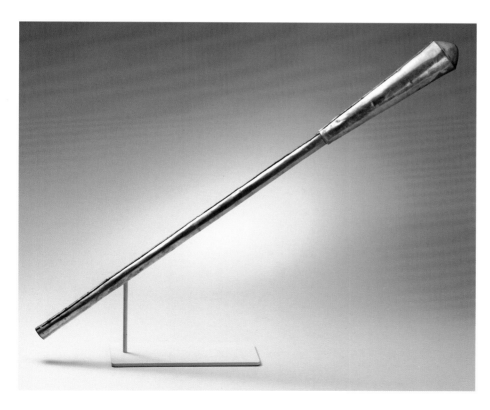

47183

CEREMONIAL WAR CLUB

Moche
100 B.C.–A.D. 500
Gold sheathing over (?) wood
Length 36⁷⁄₈ in. Diameter 2³⁄₄ in.

See description in Lot 47181.

Provenance
Splendors of the World, Haiku, Hawaii

Estimate: $14,000-$16,000

47184

SPEAR THROWER WITH EFFIGY OF A STANDING WARRIOR

Moche
A.D. 100–600
Copper
Length 13 in. Width 1⅞ in.

This spear thrower is made of three components: a fabricated rolled tube, a cast dart hook, and an elaborately-developed cast thumb rest. Brads were used to attach the cast pieces to the shaft, and impressions in the age patination indicate that the dart hook was further stabilized with a cord wrapping. The thumb rest shows an armed warrior standing on a platform. His complex headdress includes a crescent-shaped centerpiece with a mask at its base, while behind this is a war club head amid three bowl-shaped forms. From the front the side two bowl-shapes are in part visible below the blade. The warrior wears a tunic, which once showed checkerboard divisions. A war club is propped against his left arm and a circular shield with central boss against his right. In his raised hands he holds two pointed objects reminiscent of the bags carried by runners in various painted representations. A flap hangs down from his back, with an eroded projection centered on his back. The whole may originally have shown an animal pelt pouch. Green encrusted age patination covers the spear thrower, with rust at the jointure of thumb rest and shaft.

Provenance
Splendors of the World, Haiku, Hawaii

Estimate: $2,000-$2,500

47185

TUMI TOPPED BY AN ANIMAL EFFIGY

Moche
A.D. 100–600
Copper, turquoise or chrysacola
Height 5⅞ in. Width 1¼ in.

Miniature cast copper effigies and scenes are one of the outstanding accomplishments of Moche artist-craftsmen. One favored context for these castings was at the top of small-sized examples of the type of chopping knife known as a *tumi*. In this one an unexpected conjunction of animal and activity occurs: a square-headed, snarling feline is show performing the burden-carrying function of a llama: eight minute sealed vessels are stacked, four to a side, on the animal's back. Green stone inlays (either turquoise or chrysacola) pick up details of the head and form a decorative band around the rectangular base on which the animal stands. A somewhat crusty green age patination covers the entire surface.

Provenance
Splendors of the World, Haiku, Hawaii

Estimate: $1,000-$1,400

47186

SMALL SPATULA

Moche
A.D. 100–600
Copper
Height 7⅛ in. Width ⅞ in.

This small spatula is topped by an integrally cast portrayal of a battle-ready warrior standing on an L-shaped frame set within an open, roofed structure reminiscent of a guard box. The warrior wears a crescent-shaped helmet with central mask and a prominent crescent-shaped nose ornament, while his detailed right hand supports a knob-headed war club. A small round shield hides the left hand. A minute detail which indicates Moche interest in showing how things were actually made lies in the side beams that hold the slightly upward-sloped roof in place. There is a small suspension loop at back just below the floor of the structure. The crusty green age patination has a few patches of rust.

Provenance
Splendors of the World, Haiku, Hawaii

Estimate: $800-$1,200

47187

PENDANT, SEATED WARRIOR

Moche
A.D. 100–500
Gold, Weight 6 grams
Height 1¼ in. Width 2⅛ in.

This miniature gold piece shows a seated figure
wearing a two-tiered crown. Each segment of the
crown is bordered by heat-welded beads, while
the figure proper has been fabricated from several
pieces. The minute face is formed by repoussé. Small
horizontal elements at the rear waist hold suspended
danglers. The figure holds a club horizontally in front
of his knees. A skull caps the right end of this club. The
overall condition is good, with minor surface staining.

Provenance
Lawrence Witten, New Haven
Splendors of the World, Haiku, Hawaii

Estimate: $1,500-$2,500

47188

TWEEZERS SURMOUNTED BY A PROFILE ANIMAL FIGURE

Moche
A.D. 100–500
Gold, traces of red pigment, Weight 0.8 grams
Height 1⅝ in. Width 1⁵⁄₁₆ in.

Small gold tweezers with a top loop allowing for suspension on a
cord formed a part of upper classic regalia in Moche Peru. With
bold silhouetting and a few simple repoussé elements, a surprisingly
lively profile animal has been created atop the broad tweezer area.
Other than minor surface stains, the condition is good.

Provenance
Splendors of the World, Haiku, Hawaii

Estimate: $1,500-$2,500

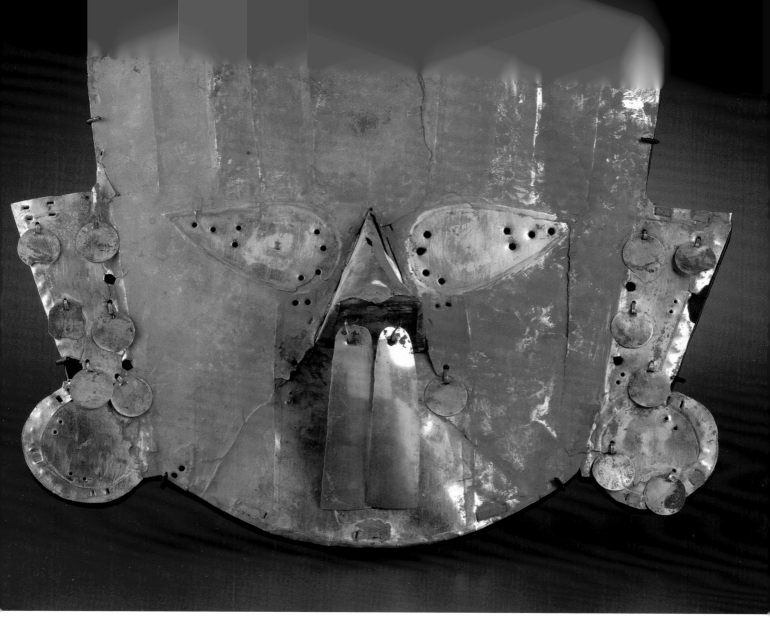

47189

FACE MASK

Sicán
A.D. 700–1100
Gold, red pigment
Height 8½ in. Width 12½ in.

This gold face mask is of the kind most frequently found in Sicán sites. The masks were conceived to have convexly-flexed facial areas with flattened ear flanges. The eye, and possibly ear spool, areas would have had attached pieces covered with a mosaic of iridescent hummingbird feathers (Junius Bird, personal communication). At some point in its funerary role the present mask was repeatedly folded for ritual reasons, resulting in the series of vertical creases, with a few crack lines, visible today. The mask had been covered with red pigment in the traditional manner which left the mouth and chin area bare. During recent restoration a considerable amount of repigmentation was done. Danglers are ranged along the ear flanges, with some now missing. There are numerous small crack areas on the mask.

Provenance
Bonhams & Butterfields, San Fransisco: sale 7546E, 14 June 2004, lot 1069, p. 23

Estimate: $10,000-$15,000

47190

PAIR OF GOLD AND SILVER EARSPOOLS

Sicán
A.D. 700–1100
Gold, silver-sheathed incised ear tubes
(A) Diameter 2⅛ in.
(B) Diameter 2⅛ in.

Comprising in all two gold repoussé disks and two silver tubular bars with incised designs, it is uncertain from surviving corrosion patterns whether or not the units were originally integral. The gold disks, one of which has a large splotch of cuprous corrosion adhering to the figure's torso, depict standing regal figures wearing large crescent-shaped headdresses and holding cups. They wear ear ornaments and tunics with zigzag borders. Closely-set lines radiate outward along the arcs of their headdresses. Outside a raised rim, a row of bead-forms with outwardly dependent elements borders the whole. The silver tubes have several rows of repoussé geometric designs bordering each end. Both silver pieces have considerable corrosion and an end piece is missing from one. A few further small corrosion spots are on the gold disks.

Provenance
Splendors of the World, Haiku, Hawaii

Estimate: $4,000-$6,000

47191

BOWL WITH FIVE REPOUSSÉ FIGURES

Sicán
Silver-Gilt, Weight 202 grams
A.D. 700–1100
Height 2⅞ in. Diameter 9⅜ in.

As seen when the bowl is set on a surface, the repoussé frontal figures are hardly visible. The ray forms arcing above their heads alone are fully visible, creating an effect paralleling that of the sun surfacing at the horizon. Only when the bowl is tilted does one see fully the greatly simplified frontal figures, standing in a framework which probably represents in a conceptual fashion a wooden royal carrying chair, examples of which have been found. Sketchily rendered outward facing animal forms beside the figures' hands may be a part of the décor of the carrying chair. The full-faced individuals wear a notched headpiece, above which the standard crescent-shaped crown may be seen, its upper edge divided into radiating segments. There is a pressure impression along eight-and-one-half inches of the top circumference, resulting in cracking at one point. There is some exterior surface staining and minor scratches. The interior has heavier surface stains with corrosion and cuprous deposits at some points.

Provenance
Splendors of the World, Haiku, Hawaii

Estimate: $4,000-$6,000

47192

DOUBLE-WALLED CEREMONIAL BOWL

Sicán
A.D. 700–1100
Silver, red paint, Weight 182 grams
Height 2¾ in. Diameter 7¾ in.

In this double-walled bowl, the interior wall was hammered to a size large enough that it could extend at an angle outward from its topmost level to form the flat upper rim. It was then lapped over to create a joint with the exterior wall just below this rim. The excellent craftsmanship with which this was done gives the vessel a finely finished appearance. The repoussé design was executed on the outer wall before the two were joined. This interesting décor represents rather large displayed lobster monsters among flying birds. A double circle is in the center base. An ancient repair, now covered by a layer of corrosion, is visible inside, extending two-and-three-fourths of an inch along the rim. There is some cracking with minor losses, and at least one modern fill is on the exterior. There is heavy corrosion inside, with moderate corrosion outside. In a number of places both inside and outside, especially nearer the rim, there are intermittent residues of the original viscous red paint coating.

Provenance
Splendors of the World, Haiku, Hawaii

Estimate: $4,000-$6,000

47193

DIADEM AND PECTORAL

Sihuas
A.D. 100–300
Gold
Diadem Height 6⅛ in. Width 6 in.
Pectoral Height 4½ in. Width 5¾ in.

While a series of diadems made of thin embossed gold sheets and closely related to this example have been published in an article devoted to the type (Colin McEwan and Joerg Haeberli, "Ancestors Past but Present. Gold Diadems from the Far South Coast of Peru," in Colin McEwan. *Precolumbian Gold Technology, Style and Iconography.* Chicago: Fitzroy Dearborn Publishers, 2000, pp.16-27.), parallels for the trapezoidal companion piece (probably a pectoral) have not been published. The diadem shape is reminiscent of a bird silhouette, but lacking the head. Executed in a broad repoussé technique, both diadem and pectoral have as the central motif a greatly-simplified frontal face with large eyes, rudimentary nose and mouth, and vertical strips in the chin area that suggest a beard. The diadem is bordered by circular bosses and its crown area has a human face similar to the main one. The principal face has a large beaded forehead band and beaded streamers along the sides of the face. The central face of the pectoral, located in the top center area, is sketchily presented, but noticeable pupils have been added to the eyes. Both pieces have a few small age tears along the edges. The lower edge of the diadem was probably folded, leaving it creased and wrinkled, with stains in its lower proper right area.

Provenance
Bonhams & Butterfields, San Francisco: sale 7477E, 8 December 2003, lot 3066, pp.20-21 (there mounted with a feather-covered band being offered as a separate lot in the present sale)

Estimate: $8,000-$12,000

47194

PLUMED HEADDRESS ORNAMENT

Huari
A.D. 500–750
Gold, Weight 22 grams
Height 8⅝ in. Width 3¾ in.

Three central vertical plumes terminate in repoussé upward-facing feline heads. Five circular openings arc across below, these enclosed at the outer edges by lobe-shaped outward projections, each ending in a downward-facing repoussé animal head, from which a ridged neck extends to the plume bases. Paired small punches are above each circular opening. The tapered lower area is plain, and narrows to a long flattened pin-form. The surface is wrinkled in several areas and has minor staining. There are small tears where the plumes meet the central portion of the ornament. Otherwise the condition is very good.

Provenance
Sotheby's, New York: sale 7996, 14 May 2004, lot 108, p.103

Estimate: $3,000-$4,000

47195

HEADDRESS WITH EAR ORNAMENTS

Paracas
A.D. 100–700
Gold, traces of red pigment
Height (as mounted) 13½ in. Diameter 7¾ in.

This headdress is an impressive assembly of gold ornaments. The crown head band forms a 2½ inch wide circle having pierced Greek-style crosses with four embossed roundels that mark each quadrant. A 7¼ inch high plume with a repoussé design of four rows of complimentary triangles adorning a broad top edge is attached by brads to the circlet. The plume, which still retains traces of red pigment that were rubbed onto the gold, may represent a feather. Concave circular discs are attached to each side of the crown. They too are embossed with roundels on their rims. Surfaces of all the components have some deposits and corrosion. Areas of assembly have some modern reinforcement.

Provenance
Bonhams & Butterfields, San Francisco: sale 7546E, 14 June 2003, lot 1065, p.20

Estimate: $8,000-$12,000

47196

BREASTPLATE AND DISK

Chimú
A.D. 1100 – 1400
Silver
Breastplate Height 4⅞ in. Width 6⁹⁄₁₆ in.
Disc Diameter 4½ in.

The principle repoussé patterns on these two pieces are schematically-rendered profile birds with large beaks. On the breastplate these are divided by a small center space (in which four attachment holes were punched in a square format) so that each group of four birds faces inward. A finely-scaled beaded band edges the entire breastplate. On the disk, six similar birds move in the same direction along a broad outer band. Inside this a groove separates a central raised area which once was completed by a centrally-attached ornament. The upper ends of the breastplate are wrinkled, perhaps the result of folding. The stained surface is in relatively good condition.

Provenance
Bonhams & Butterfields, San Francisco: sale 7437E, 9 June 2003, lot 5109, p.26 (there shown mounted with additional items: silver plume and mother-of-pearl disk)

Estimate: $2,000-$3,000

47197

HEAD BAND AND PAIR OF SMALLER BANDS

Chimú
A.D. 1100 -1400
Silver
Crown Band Height 1¹¹⁄₁₆ in. Length 25 in.
Ear Spool Heights 1¾ – ⅝ in. Lengths 9 – 9¼ in.

The exact original use of these matching silver bands is uncertain. The repoussé patterns of all three – large bosses between bands of raised beading – are the same. This and their width correspondences support the suggestion that they were made originally to be used together. The condition is fair, with minor cracks and stains. Small punctures along all edges indicate that they were once attached to some other support.

Provenance
Bonhams & Butterfields, San Francisco: sale 7437E, 9 June 2003, lot 5109, p.26 (There shown mounted with addition items.)

Estimate: $3,000-$4,000

47198

PAIR OF EARSPOOLS

Chimú
A.D. 1100–1400
Wood, shell, green stone
Weight 50 grams
Diameter 2½ in.

A standard North Coast motif
from Moche times onward
for a thousand years presents a
standing frontal figure holding
objects to either side and wearing
a large crescent-shaped headdress.
In these earspools each figure
holds a pair of what appear to
be tall cups with white upper
sections, orange central areas, and
blue-green lower parts. The faces
have noses carved in bas-relief.
This feature combines with blue-
green eyes to impart a surprising
degree of animation in such small
faces. There is some cracking and minor loss in the wood. The mosaic is in good condition, with
minor adhesive losses and surface abrasions.

Provenance
Bonhams & Butterfields, San Francisco: sale 737E, 9 June 2003, lot 5110 (there mounted with a
silver-repoussé crown and breastplate, no longer a part of the present lot)

Estimate: $4,000-$6,000

47199

BEAKER WITH HUMAN FACE AND ARMS

Late Horizon
A.D. 1100–1400
Silver with surface gilt band
Height 4⁹⁄₁₆ in. Diameter 2³⁄₈ in.

Several elements make this face cup unusual. The most
striking is the band of gilding that runs at a slight right-to-
left descending diagonal through the center face, across the
bottom, and up the back. Also noticeable are the grinning
mouth with prominent teeth and the presence of small-scaled
arms and hands. The condition is fair, with cracking and
losses at the rim and other areas stabilized.

Provenance
Splendors of the World, Haiku, Hawaii

Estimate: $2,000-$2,500

47200

TUMI

Chimú
A.D. 1000–1350
Copper
Height 11¼ in. Width 5½ in.

Both front and back of the handle portion of this heavy copper *tumi* are covered with incised imagery. The front side, as mounted, has a columnar arrangement of three schematically-rendered standing frontal figures with wavy, upward-streaming hair. They hold war clubs in each hand and wear large earspools. The central figures are bordered at the sides and top by a band of rectangles containing a repeated pattern. The back side of the handle has a similar stacked arrangement of three collared masks (or highly conventionalized faces) with a centrally divided outward arching headdress or coiffure. In addition to a similar border, each head is separated from the next by a decorated band, with a bottom filler area divided vertically into several bands. There is overall age patination as well as corrosion and incrustation, especially on the knife blade area, the edges of which are slightly ragged from corrosion losses.

Provenance
Bonhams & Butterfields, San Francisco: sale 7477E, 8 December 2003, lot 3067, p.22, ill.22

Estimate: $1,200-$1,800

47201

DOUBLE-SPOUT BRIDGE-HANDLE VESSEL

Central Coast, Peru
A.D. 400–800
Buff ceramic, slip
Height 10½ in. Width (at spout) 6⅜ in.

Two uses of slips are combined in this vessel. The slipped areas on the body of the vessel in buff, white, and brownish-red are burnished, while the areas of rapidly executed broad white-line work (which include the schematic figure inside the structure) remain unburnished. A shed-roofed structure with front corner posts is incorporated into the upper vessel body. Inside this a rapidly brushed figure with spread arms and legs is placed as though seated. Only the nose has been modeled three-dimensionally, contrasting with the otherwise wholly painted décor. The vessel is in sound condition, with minor repairs to the proper left of the structure.

Provenance
Bonhams & Butterfields, San Francisco: sale 7437E, 9 June 2003, lot 5079, pp.18–19

Estimate: $300-$400

47202

STIRRUP-SPOUT ARCHITECTURAL VESSEL

Sicán
A.D. 700–1100
Burnished orangeware
Height 8 in. Width 4½ in. Depth 3⅜ in.

A rectangular, three-level structure is shown, with visually balanced ramps leading to the different levels. Summarily-executed figures are seated at the proper right of level one and at the top proper left spout base. Since much of the architecture of north coastal valley sites was adobe-built and thus survives only in badly eroded condition, such representations help to give a sense of the architectural setting of Late Intermediate Period life. Both figures are missing most of the right arm and leg, and are generally abraded. There are minor chips at the spout.

Provenance
Bonhams & Butterfields, San Francisco: sale 7437E, 9 June 2003, lot 5077, pp. 18–19

Estimate: $600-$900

47203

SINGLE-SPOUT STRAP-HANDLE VESSEL

Chimú
A.D. 1100–1400
Burnished blackware
Height 8⅝ in. Depth 7 in.

The scene at the front of the vessel shows an open shed supported at the front corners by columns. Inside a figure wearing an overhanging headdress and large earspools is seated crosslegged on a mat. A small offering bowl is in front of him on the mat. The back of the roof has a notched vertical flange, and a raised band terminates the front of the roof. In overall good condition, the vessel has small chips at spout rim, strap edge, and flanged base.

Provenance
Bonhams & Butterfields, San Francisco: sale 7437E, 9 June 2003, lot 5088, pp.20–21

Estimate: $1,000-$1,200

47204

FIGURAL VESSEL

Chancay
A.D. 1000–1350
Ceramic with cream, black, and pale rust slip
Height 20⅜ in. Diameter 31 in.

The low-relief legs of this globular vessel indicate that the individual holding a small cup is seated. A broad collar is incised in roughly rectangular units. The headband has a series of notched projections interspersed with dark brown vertical bands. The figure has elaborate facial paint and wears large loop earspools. There is minor restoration with areas of overpaint.

Provenance
Bonhams & Butterfields, San Francisco: sale 7477E, 8 December 2003, lot 3041, p.16

Estimate: $1,200-$1,800

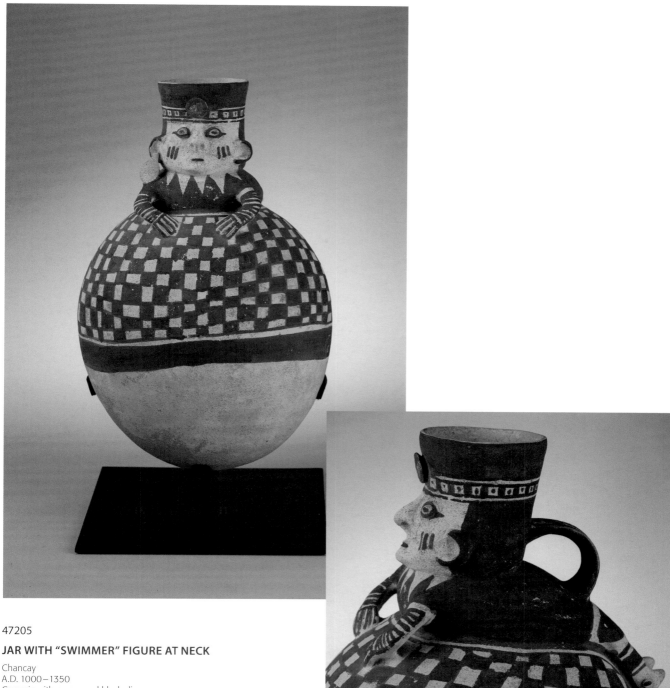

47205

JAR WITH "SWIMMER" FIGURE AT NECK

Chancay
A.D. 1000–1350
Ceramic with cream and black slip
Height 16½ in. Diameter 31⅞ in.

This egg-shaped vessel is unusual among Chancay matte-painted figural jars in its black and white checkerboard upper half, and even more in the small complete figure shown lying on its stomach with arms and legs projecting forward and back. The individual's head forms the spout and a loop handle emerges from his back. He wears a single pendant earring in his right ear, while his headdress has a band at bottom and central circular medallion. The condition is good, with slight surface paint loss.

Provenance
Bonhams & Butterfields, San Francisco: sale 7546E, 14 June 2004, lot 1078, p.26

Estimate: $2,000-$3,000

47206

VESSEL WITH FIGURE HOLDING CUP

Chancay
A.D. 1000–1350
Ceramic with white, rust, and dark brown slip
Height 16¾ in. Diameter 26⅜ in.

Three colors of slip—white, rust, and dark brown—join low-relief modeling to define the figure embodied in this vessel. A seated position is indicated by the white low relief legs, the proper left one bearing a double band at the knee area and both with ankle bands. Similar bands are on upper and lower arms and at the wrists. Fingers and toes are schematically defined, as are eyes, chinstrap, and headband. The small cup is of the same white slip as the upper half of the figure. The bold upward-moving points at the outer eye are reminiscent of the more northerly Sicán style, which may have some chronological overlap with the central coastal style known as Chancay. There are minor restorations and areas of overpaint.

Provenance
Bonhams & Butterfields, San Francisco: sale 7546E, 14 June 2004, lot 1079, p.26

Estimate: $1,200-$1,800

47207

FIGURAL VESSEL

Chancay
A.D. 1000–1350
Ceramic with black and cream slip
Height 14⅞ in. Diameter 27⅞ in.

The painted additions to the low-relief eyes give this figure a startled expression which the mouth-area paint reinforces. Textile patterns are painted on a head band and on the arms, and a frontal disk pendant is indicated by negative painting. There is a single lug handle at the back. The condition is fair, with overpaint and one area of restoration.

Provenance
Bonhams & Butterfields, San Francisco: sale 7477E, 8 December 2003, lot 3044, p.16

Estimate: $1,200-$1,800

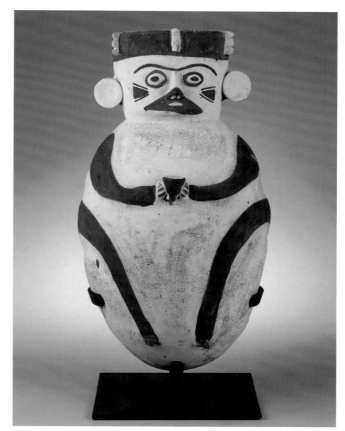

47208

TWO FIGURAL VESSELS, EACH HOLDING A CUP

Chancay
A.D. 1000–1350
Ceramic with black and cream slip
(A) Height 19 in. Diameter 28¾ in.
(B) Height 20¼ in. Diameter 31¼ in.

Though differing in size and painted decoration, these two seated, cup-holding figures share two features: a dark headband with intermittent white notched projections and a relief-modeled four-hole flute suspended from the neck at back. Each figure has some restoration and areas of overpaint.

Provenance
Bonhams & Butterfields, San Francisco: sale 7477E, 8 December 2003, lot 3043, lot 3042, p.16

Estimate: $1,500-$2,000

47209

GLOBULAR VESSEL WITH DOUBLE-HEADED SERPENT

Paracas
400–200 B.C.
Burnished blackware, resin-based pigment
Height 9⅝ in. Diameter 9½ in.

An excellent example of the early major ceramic style of the south coast of Peru that centered around the Paracas peninsula, this vessel has an added pouring spout on the shoulder. A rich burnt orange ground covers the upper two-thirds of the globular shape. Into this a bold, undulating double-headed serpent-form has been incised. The heads are shown as the large-eyed image with grinning mouth known as the Oculate Being, the chins ending in goatee-like points. Each head has three symmetrical whisker-like tufts at ear and chin area, and there are short two-toed front legs on the body near each head. Two-unit rust and yellow tabs project periodically from the connecting body, which is outlined by a band of dark orange. Small rectangles punctuate the back along the spinal position. All of the design surfaces are resin-painted in tones of brown, rust, burnt orange, and yellow.

Christopher B. Donnan gives an excellent description of Paracas ceramic surface decoration (Christopher B. Donnan. *Ceramics of Ancient Peru.* Los Angeles: University of California, 1992, p. 35): "Designs were incised on the surface of the vessel while the clay was still moist and fairly soft. The incision was done with a dull pointed tool that created the outline and defined each area where a distinct color was to be applied once the object was fired. Most Paracas ceramics, including all those that were to be painted with resin paint, were fired in a smudging atmosphere, creating a dark gray-to-black surface.

"Resin paint was the hallmark of Paracas pottery. It was always applied after firing, and as flat color, with no attempt at blending or shading to create subtle differences of tone. Each color filled the entire area within the border of incised lines." When well-preserved, as in the present example, Paracas resin paints give a virtually unique surface, lustrous and silken, with an almost skin-like body. Colors have unusual saturation and brilliance.

The condition here is good, with scattered paint losses and repaired cracks.

Provenance
David Bernstein, New York

Estimate: $8,000-$9,000

47210

TALL BOWL

Nasca
A.D. 300–500
Polychrome ceramic
Height 7½ in. Diameter 5 in.

Below an exterior rim band decorated in connected lozenges with center circles, the vessel body is densely covered with a pair of painted monstrous creatures, one above the other. These swim in a sea of blood, which has probably issued from their maws, and their many-segmented bodies are covered with trophy-head hairs. Overall small-scale flaking of slip, with one larger loss area near the bottom, is visible and there is one hairline crack from the rim downward.

Provenance
Bonhams & Butterfields, San Francisco: sale 7477E, 8 December 2003, lot 3046, pp. 16,17

Estimate: $1,000-$1,500

47211

BOWL WITH FLARING SIDES

Nasca
100 B.C.–A.D. 250
Polychrome ceramic
Diameter 9¼ in.

With an unslipped interior, the flaring low bowl has an even white slip on its exterior that bears two bands of design, the upper wider and more complex than the lower. Four outstretched deities "swim" around the upper with their tongues extended from whiskered mouths. Masks trailing streamers, all with strands of trophy-head hair, complete the upper body. The lower bodies are simplified and anthropomorphic. Below a dividing band hang identical plant-derived forms

in varying color combinations. The overall condition is fair, with one large crack through the face of a deity and minute chips in the slip.

Provenance
John-Platt Collection (Daniel M. Friedenberg)
Sotheby's, NY: sale 7902, 15 May 2003, lot 269, p.182

Published
Von Winning, Hasso, *The John-Platt Collection of Pre-Columbian Art*, Charlottesville: The University of Virginia Art Museum, 1986, p.112, ill.249

Estimate: $2,500-$3,500

47212

PAIR OF FIGURATIVE VESSELS

Nasca
A.D. 300–500
Polychrome Ceramic
(A) Height 8¼ in.
(B) Height 8 in.

Almost identical vessels show seated individuals holding plants. Each wears a hood with a raised crest toward front center along which are painted seed forms. Both hold three plant stalks in the right hand and a pepino with its stem in the left. On a cord around the neck a bean-like pod is suspended, a double unit on one figure, a single on the other. This latter figure has the soles of its feet indicated in outline on the vessel bottom. The painting is done quite freely. The figure with soles of feet indicated has some chipping and repaired crack systems, as well as a paint loss on the proper right leg.

Provenance
Butterfields, San Francisco: sale 7376E, 18 November 2002, lot 1098/2, p.22

Estimate: $4,000-$6,000

47213

DOUBLE-SPOUT STRAP-HANDLE VESSEL

Nasca
100 B.C.–A.D. 250
Polychrome ceramic
Height 5¾ in. Width 5⅝ in.

On this vessel the shift in curvature occurs low in the profile, which leaves the majority of the upper surface free for imagery. Two similar masked warriors are shown; each holds a spear thrower in his right hand and two trophy heads in the left. There is some minor inpainting on small pocked areas; waxed surface.

Provenance
John-Platt Collection (Daniel M. Friedenberg)
Sotheby's, New York: sale 7902, 15 May 2003, lot 271, p.182

Published
Von Winning, Hasso, *The John-Platt Collection of Pre-Columbian art,*Charlottesville: The University of Virginia Art Museum, 1986, pp.110-111, ill.244

Estimate: $2,000-$3,500

47214

SINGLE-SPOUT STRAP-HANDLE VESSEL

Nasca
100 B.C.–A.D. 250
Polychrome ceramic
Height 5⅞ in. Width 7½ in.

The broad, low-contoured vessel has an upright, forward-facing human head rendered in the round in lieu of one spout. A painted bib-like shape with square hatching below the head and the opposite spout defines the space of the figure. The large remaining spaces on either upper surface show profile mythologized monkeys surrounded by disembodied symbolic emblems. A band of freely rendered alternating pairs of reddish and black rectangular shapes lies along the bend of the vessel's profile. The vessel is chipped at the top of the spout, but otherwise good, with no waxing. A small spot was drilled in the bottom to take a clay sample.

Provenance
Sotheby's, New York: sale 7902, 15 May 2003, lot 271, p.182

Estimate: $2,500-$3,000

47215

STANDING FEMALE FIGURE

Huari
A.D. 500–750
Polychrome ceramic
Height 8½ in. Width 2½ in.

The generally tubular figure stands on short legs with flanged feet, with painted arms emerging from knobbed shoulders and terminating in hands with the splayed fingers meeting at the stomach. Facial features and ears are defined in low relief, the eyes then painted open wide. Tri-colored streamers flow down each cheek from the eyes. A crescent-shaped gorget is painted on. The esteem in which the figure was held anciently is indicated by repairs reattaching the head using a series of drilled holes and intricate lashing, of which much of the original cord remains. Surface crackle systems appear at several places, along with overall minor surface abrasions and chips at nose and feet.

Provenance
Bonhams & Butterfields, San Francisco: sale 7477E, 8 December 2003, lot 3047, p.17

Estimate: $800-$1,200

47216

PORTRAIT CUP

Huari
A.D. 500–750
Polychrome ceramic
Height 5 in. Width 5½ in.

The head is formed by the entire cup, with the detail of low relief features and painted elements focused on the front area. Only the hair of the subject is shown on the rear. Below a head band with three lozenge-shaped elements separated by pairs of small circles an elaborately painted face with wide, staring eyes looks straight forward. A central vertical band passes down the forehead and nose to cross the slightly crooked mouth, ending at the lower edge of the chin. On each cheek rectangles with paired hooked shapes are shown in alternating color schemes. The simple, flange-like ears are painted with three circles on the left and two on the right. The overall condition is good, with minor paint losses. The proper right ear was broken and reattached. A small drill hole is behind the proper left ear.

Provenance
Bonhams & Butterfields, San Francisco: sale 7477E, 8 December 2003, lot 3048, p.17

Estimate: $1,000-$1,500

47217

STANDING FEMALE FIGURE

Central Coast (Peru)
A.D. 900–1400
Buff ceramic; Paint; Cord wrapping; Loose weave fabric garment
Height 18⁷⁄₁₆ in. Width 6½ in.

The plump naked female figure holds her spread hands against her chest. Her broad feet are joined at the arch by a hollow bridge. A lightly indicated navel is above a strongly indicated pubic triangle, while an incised horizontal line defines a collarbone ridge. The trapezoidal head with flattened top bears strongly modeled features, with an especially prominent aquiline nose. Relief eyebrows, eye rims, and eyes are painted black. Ear openings served as air escapes during firing. Along the top edge of the head pairs of holes, centered and at either side, still have partial cord ties remaining. A roll of slightly twisted cords is around the neck. Rolls of cord around either ankle are knotted at front. Toes and fingers are indicated by incised slashes.

Provenance
Dave DeRoche, Piedmont, California

Estimate: $1,200-$1,800

47218

SNUFF PALETTE

Huari/Tiwanaku
A.D. 500–1100
Gray slate with red inclusions, Weight 344 grams
Height 7 in. Width 3¹⁵⁄₁₆ in.

The complexity of the shaped snuff palette is closest in format, style, and motifs to those in examples related to Huari and late Tiwanaku contexts. While most of those are wood, a few of these stone examples do exist. From an axe-shaped handle a rectangular holder extends, the center roughly hollowed out and the borders covered with loosely incised geometric patterns. A slightly-raised band at the outer edge has an incised fret design. On this stand two outward-facing profile animals with squared-off heads and looped tails into which something could have been tied. The visual effect is enhanced by rich red mineral inclusions in the gray slate. The condition is excellent.

Provenance
Arte Textil (Steve Berger), San Francisco, California

Estimate: $3,000-$4,000

47219

STANDING DIGNITARY

Sicán
A.D. 700–1100
Wood
Height 7¼ in. Width 4⅛ in.

A fully frontal figure stands with hands in front of the chest, the right holding a cup. Wearing a large crescent-shaped headdress with rows of incised patterning, the large-eyed figure is possibly masked. Circular ear ornaments with beaded borders hang from the headdress, and he wears a three-strand necklace. Tabs thrust outward from each shoulder. Below the tunic, legging-like elements cover the legs. The edges of these and the tunic are carved as if representing an edging of triangular dangles. The toes and toenails are carefully delineated. The condition is good.

Provenance
Splendors of the World, Haiku, Hawaii

Estimate: $1,200-$1,800

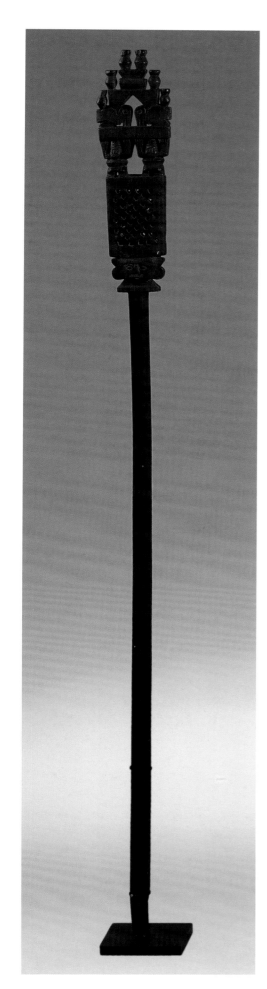

47220

CARVED CEREMONIAL STAFF WITH EFFIGY RATTLE TOP

Chimú
A.D. 1110–1400
Wood, seeds, traces of original red paint
Height 54½ in. Width 4½ in.
Height (top effigy components) 14½ in.

The two broad faces of this ceremonial staff are identical. Serving to base the widened rattle area, a simplified frontal bust of a deity with stylized ears and earspool flanges rests atop the long circular shaft. On his head a rectangular carved openwork area, gridded diagonally, contains dried seed rattles. Two small atlantean figures stand on this supporting a bar on which inward-facing birds crouch, their beaks touching the bar. The birds support a three-tiered superstructure, each side holding a jar on each of its two ascending tiers, with two jars capping the entire arrangement. An indented area at the shaft's lower end indicates that it was once tipped by a metal element. The condition is excellent.

Provenance
Splendors of the World, Haiku, Hawaii
Christie's, Paris: sale 5068, 10 December 2003, lot 417, p.114

Estimate: $4,000-$6,000

47221

RECTANGULAR COVERED TREASURE BOX

Chimú
A.D. 1000 -1350
Wood with colored pigment
Box: Height 3¼ in. Width 3¼ in. Length 8 in.
Lid: Height 1 in. Width 3⅞ in. Length 8¾ in.

This covered wooden box is in an exceptional
state of preservation, retaining much colored
pigment which had been rubbed into areas
acting as a ground for the shallow two-
level relief design. The principal image is a
repeated square-framed stylized profile figure
shown seated with leg forward. The person
shown wears a large two-part arced headdress
supported by a skullcap, this all presented as a
frontal view on the profile head. A trapezoidal
fan shape projects at the figure's back,
probably a rear flap like that worn by earlier
Moche warriors. Each figure holds a tasseled
bag. Banded borders are filled with a variety of
repeated forms, including a step-fret-and-curl
and a profile bird's head. Colors included at
least turquoise, orange, and white.

Provenance
David Bernstein, New York

Estimate: $4,500-$6,000

47222

TRUMPET WITH HUMAN HEAD EFFIGY

Moche
A.D. 100–600
Wood with shell and green stone inlay
Length 26½ in. Diameter 2⅜ in.

This ceremonial effigy trumpet, made from a heavy coarse-grained wood, has a simplified low relief human head a short distance below the mouthpiece. The eyes are inlaid with shell and greenstone, with "tear" bands descending the cheeks inlaid in spondylus shell terminating in white shell profile animal heads. Small greenstone circles serve as ear ornaments. An inlaid headband of mixed spondylus and white shell has a minute central, highly stylized mask formed of greenstone and shell, its greenstone rectangle carved with a low relief eye-nose unit. There is an overall age patination to the wood, with minor cracking midway down and some small ancient surface loss. Two triangular inlays are missing from the headband. The abraded mouth area shows evidence of having originally been inlaid.

Provenance
Splendors of the World, Haiku, Hawaii

Estimate: $4,000-$6,000

47223

TWO WAR CLUBS

Late Horizon
A.D. 1300–1530
(A, B) Copper alloy, wood, rawhide
(A) Length 17½ in. Diameter of head 4 in.
(B) Length 19 in. Depth 5½ in.

Two forms of hand-held war clubs are represented here, a straight-bladed axe and the familiar star-head club. All parts appear to be of the same age and thus integral (the star-head slips off but wear patterns on the wood suggest that this is the original shaft). The copper alloy parts are in good condition, as is the wood except for a broken lower end on the star-head club. The original rawhide components are brittle and abraded.

Provenance
Arte Textil (Steve Berger), San Francisco, California

Estimate: $2,000-$3,000

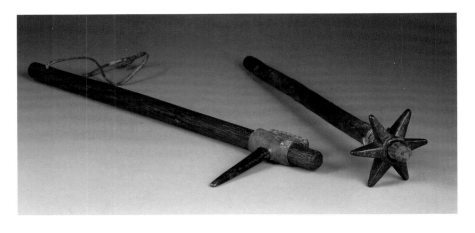

47224

FOUR SPEAR THROWERS IN THEIR ORIGINAL TEXTILE BAG

Central Coast, Peru
A.D. 900–1400
(A) Wood, bone, cord
    Length 18¾ in.
(B) Wood, bone, rawhide cord
    Length 19½ in.
(C) Bone with paint, bitumen, fiber, copper
    Length 20½ in.
(D) Wood, rawhide, bronze
    Length 18⅜ in.

The four spear throwers were reportedly found together in this striped textile bag. Three have wood shafts, while the fourth is of bone. The bone shaft has a plain wooden thumb hook attached. Since much of the cord in this lashing is recent, it is probably a modern assembly. Two of the wood shafts have bone thumb hooks, one shaped like a saddle horn and the other with three addorsed standing figures done in considerable detail and enhanced with pigment (these figures have recently been reattached, and a conservator's report is available with the lot). The cord lashing both bone hooks is in considerable part old, and still retains resinous infusions. The fourth, wooden-shafted thrower has a wooden thumb hook of simplified head form and a dart hook of bronze in the form of a schematic reclining figure. This latter is heavily corroded and is secured by a plant bast lashing, parts of which still adhere. This group is of historical interest, though one must preserve caution about the degrees of reassembly.

Provenance
Arte Textil, San Francisco (Steve Berger)

Estimate: $3,000-$4,000

47225

SPEAR THROWER

Moche (Early)
100 B.C. – A.D. 200
Wood, gold, lapis lazuli, shell, red pigment
Length 20 in. Depth 3⅜ in.

The major importance of this piece lies in the strong sculptural quality of the lapis lazuli thumb hook. This portrays a bird with a slightly uptilted head looking back toward its tail. Its spondylus shell eyes are framed in gold and the entire bird was originally rubbed with red pigment. The stone sculpture, the visible wood parts, and most of the gold date from the same period. The hood is modern, as is the metal end cap. The exact nature of reassemblage cannot be assessed without x-ray photographs.

A conservator's report will be available to the purchaser.

Provenance
Splendors of the World, Haiku, Hawaii

Estimate: $7,000-$10,000

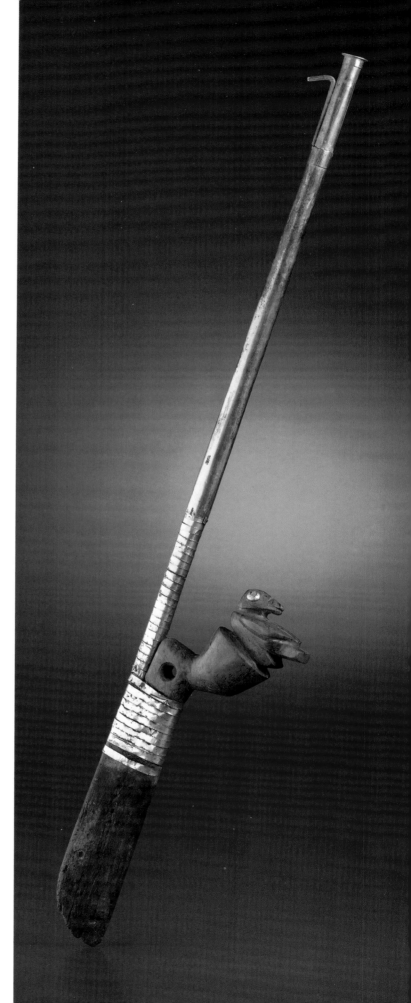

47226

QERO WITH INWARD-CURVING RIM

Inca/Colonial
A.D. 1500–1650
Wood, pigment
Height 6⅛ in. Diameter 5½ in.

This rather thick-walled wooden *qero* has an elegant, inward-curving rim, around which is a broad band of incised traditional motifs inlaid in color. The most visible of these is a winged insect seen from above, with yellow antennae, orange triangular upper wings, and yellow triangular lower. Alternating with these are angled snakes with heads toward the rim and profile facing pairs of yellow-spotted dark felines. The condition is generally good, with two large cracks. One starts at the rim and a contiguous loss area partially obscures a cat. The other crack runs upward from the bottom.

Provenance
David Bernstein, New York

Estimate: $3,500-$4,500

47227

RECTANGULAR CLOTH WITH ALTERNATING BIRD HEADS

Chavín
800-400 B.C.
Cotton fiber and pigment
Length 26½ in. Width 12¼ in.

The rarity of textiles with Chavín imagery gives each example importance. Almost all pieces that do survive are, as this one, painted with deft brushwork on finely woven cotton fabric. This textile is unusual among Chavín painted textiles in its general boldness and simplicity of abstract design, and in the arrangement of interlocked bird images within an overall grid. This latter element looks forward to of one mode of textile pattern organization which became key in many later weaving traditions. The simplified birds' heads have eyes like those also seen in Chavín snake representations. Since much Chavín iconography is filled with double−and even triple−level imagery, this resonance was almost certainly intentional. The original selvage is present, along with one braided corner tie. For a textile of this age the condition is as expected. It is mounted on a fine weave fabric which is in turn sewn to a stretched fabric.

Provenance
Bonhams & Butterfields, San Francisco: sale 7437E, 9 June 2003, lot 5117, p.30

Estimate: $1,500-$3,000

47228

SEGMENT FROM A MANTLE

Paracas
300−100 B.C.
Camelid fiber, cotton
Height 87¾ in. Width 18⅛ in.

This mantle segment includes one long side of embroidered designs and small amounts of the two adjoining embroidered edges. The ground is a very dark brown plain weave and the embroidery is done in dark brown, deep red, and infrequent accents of gold. Two highly conventionalized dancer motifs alternate along the edge, and each motif repetition reverses orientation from those nearest in either direction. The condition is poor, with large loss areas in the undecorated portion as well as considerable losses in the embroidered areas.

Provenance
Bonhams & Butterfields, San Francisco: sale 7437E, 9 June 2003, lot 5132, pp.32-34, ill. p.32

Estimate: $3,000-$4,000

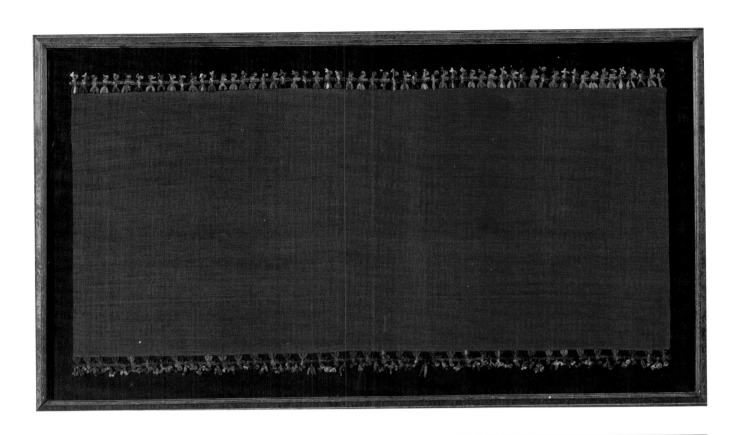

47229

MANTLE WITH KNITTED HUMMINGBIRD BORDERS

Nasca (Early)
300–100 B.C.
Camelid fibers
Length 55 in. Width 25 in.

The complex knitted border indicates that this mantle comes from the period of transition from Paracas to Nasca cultures on Peru's south coast. The brilliant cochineal red plain weave center portion is in remarkably good condition for its great age, with only one small damage spot. Although the knitted borders along the longer sides initially appear similar, they actually differ. One is comprised of a row of fifty-eight outward-facing hummingbirds knitted from eight or more variously colored fibers. The other band is comprised of

thirty-eight outward-facing and equally colorful hummingbirds alternating with at least three varieties of plants outside the connecting band which runs along the wing position of the hummingbirds. The condition is quite good, with a few missing or abraded parts of the knitted borders.

Provenance
Bonhams & Butterfields, San Francisco: sale 7437E, 9 June 2003, lot 5125, pp. 32-33

Estimate: $8,000-$12,000

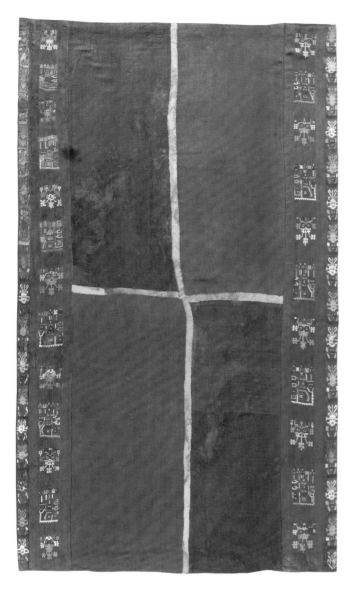

47230

LARGE MANTLE

Nasca
A.D. 300 – 500
Camelid, cotton fibers
Length 93¾ in. Width 66⅞ in.

This large mantle is complete and thus gives an idea of the overall design concept and the color interrelationships employed at the time in ancient Peru. Quadrants are established in the large central field by a cross-form band of mustard yellow. The four rectangles formed, two in maroon and two in a muted cochineal red, are set in a diagonally balanced relationship. Along the longer side of the mantle a wider inner band has complex rectangular figural motifs. These wider bands alternate two motifs: a frontal head with an elaborate gold headdress and mouth mask and a less clear highly stylized figure with several overlaid frontal heads. Each of these components exhibits typical Nasca inventiveness in varied distributions of color. The total mantle design is completed by a narrow outside band of elaborated trophy head motifs. This smaller band repeats, with a similarly inventive set of color variations, a frontal head with an elaborate full face overhead mask. The condition is fair, with variable fading on the figural images, some still preserving vivid color. There are burial stains, especially on the central plain-weave panels. There is considerable loss of fabric in the mustard-colored cross-shaped band.

Provenance
David Bernstein, New York

Estimate: $12,000-$18,000

TEXTILES FROM THE SIHUAS REGION

The three textiles given a Sihuas Valley provenance form a close iconographic and technical group. Two other closely connected examples have appeared on the market in recent years. In addition to the Sihuas Valley localization, some of the sources have given these textiles a Nasca designation, even though in iconography they are not comparable with most Nasca textiles.

All of these Sihuas Valley textiles are compositionally similar, being organized as a series of eight bars radiating from a relatively small-scaled rectangular center. Four dominant diagonal radiations create a primary X-shape, with four further, still strong radiating bars making a cross. Among the present three textiles the red-ground example centered by a stylized face with "tears" on the cheeks provides the most striking parallel to a group of interrelated highland stone relief sculptures found around Lake Titicaca.

The closest similarity is with a well-known but unprovenanced stone found about a century ago at Copacabana, Bolivia, and now in the Staatlische Museen zu Berlin, Ethnologisches Museum (Margaret Young-Sánchez, *Tiwanaku. Ancestors of the Inca*. Lincoln and London: University of Nebraska Press for Denver Art Museum, 2004, pp. 88-89). This "Carved Slab of Copacabana" is currently credited to the Yaya-Mama style and tentatively dated to 800–100 B.C. Another dramatically similar relief was found at the Bolivian site of Chiripa (Richard L. Burger. *Chavín: And the Origins of the Andean Civilization*. New York: 1992, p.220, fig. 244), which lies even closer to what became the great center of Tiwanaku. A third example of great interest is a somewhat later stone box from Pucara, dated to the ensuing Pucara style at about 200 B.C. to A.D. 200/300 (Young-Sánchez 2004, p.91). Other stone relief monuments that are strongly relevant—even more to the other two examples in this group—are the so called Arapa–Thunderbolt stela, c. 200 B.C.–A.D. 200/300 (Margaret Young-Sánchez. *Tiwanaku. Ancestors of the Inca*. Lincoln and London: University of Nebaska Press for Denver Art Museum, 2004, p.81; now divided between the northern end of Lake Titicaca and Tiwanaku proper) and the Hoyt monolith from the Capachica Peninsula, dated c. 100 B.C. to A.D. 300 (Charles Stanish. *Ancient Titicaca. The Evolution of Complex Society in Southern Peru and Northern Bolivia*. Berkley: University of California Press, 2003, p.146, fig. 7.5).

Even if one considers both geographic separation and a still uncertain time relationship, the number and consistency of similarities between the complex configurations of the stone reliefs with the equally complex design of these textiles make their cultural interrelationship convincing. To this evidence may be added the parallel of the somewhat later widespread distribution of iconographic complexes from the great highland metropolitan center of Tiwanaku, especially through the offices of the later Huari empire (A.D. 500–750).

Viewed geographically, these iconographic connections have further interest. The Sihuas Valley is far south of the core Nasca region, and only one river intervenes between Sihuas and the still further south Moquegua Valley. A look at maps in a recent study (Charles Stanish. *Ancient Titicaca. The Evolution of Complex Society in Southern Peru and Northern Bolivia*. Berkley: University of California Press, 2003, pp.9-10, maps 1.6 and 1.7) indicates Moquegua as a channel through which interaction with the Titicaca basin flowed at least during later Tiwanaku times. Linguistic studies still in progress indicate evidence for continuing interaction between these same coastal regions and the Titicaca basin (Charles Stanish. *Ancient Titicaca. The Evolution of Complex Society in Southern Peru and Northern Bolivia*. Berkley: University of California Press, 2003, p.223, maps 9.5 and 9.6).

Turning to the other two Hendershott examples, in differing color harmonies but both on white grounds and lacking the central face, their more jagged component units bring them remarkably close to two panels of the Arapa-Thunderboolt stela, the intact second-from-top unit on one side and the separated fourth-from-top unit on the other side.

A reinforcing support for all of these comparisons between stone reliefs and textiles is also found in the distribution of smaller-sized secondary components of all three textiles. These follow a patterning which exactly parallels that of the smaller-sized secondary elements on the various stone reliefs. As a group, these Sihuas Valley textiles present an iconographic system largely derived from the Titicaca basin, woven in techniques most closely related to those of the Nasca tradition centered in coastal valleys somewhat farther north.

In conclusion, one may cite the truly extraordinary Tiwanaku tapestry tunic published by Young-Sánchez (2004, pp. 46-49) and dated there to A.D. 200–400. Its central radiant face panel lies close to the iconographic lineage developed in the above discussion.

47231

LARGE RECTANGULAR PANEL WITH CENTRAL FACE

Sihuas
A.D. 100–400
Camelid, cotton fiber
Height 38¼ in. Width 63½ in.

The main design of this textile with a deep cochineal red ground is a long horizontal rectangle, centered around a conventionalized rectangular frontal face. The rectangular eyes are outlined in black and divided into diagonally-opposed quadrants of red and yellow ocher. The red mouth shows three black teeth, and there are staggered red and ocher "tear" marks on the cheeks. Eight rays emanate from the central face, the principal four moving diagonally out to near the corners (a band is reserved at either end), the secondary four forming a cross. All eight bands divide at the ends and curl back into antenna-like pairs. The diagonal rays are staggered in steps, giving them a lightning-like quality, while the horizontal and vertical rays are straight. All the rays are comprised of striped bands in dark red, yellow ocher, white, and black.

The reserved band at either end contains four geometrically conventionalized standing figures, their orientation divided at the horizontal axis so that one sees two figures upright and two upside-down. The feet indicate movement outward toward the edge. A raised "right" arm is balanced by an upraised, striped tail, imparting a monkey-like quality. Their strong, angled outlines give them an abstract skeletal appearance.

Subordinate in the main field are four spiders, placed in the triangular spaces at the sides of the vertical rays. The legs of each pair of spiders are oriented to the textile edges. White being the principal color used, the spiders stand out with vibrant prominence. Small lozenges formed of variously-colored squares are scattered across the ground as fillers. Braided ties at the four corners indicate that the textile was used in some way as clothing or stretched and tied as a wall covering—perhaps both.

The condition is fair, with none of the patches or renewals altering the integrity of the original design. Major replacement areas are in the lower right quadrant, with scattered further patches and staining visible primarily on the right side.

Provenance
Westermann Collection, Germany (1950s–70s)
Splendors of the World, Haiku, Hawaii

Estimate: $10,000-$15,000

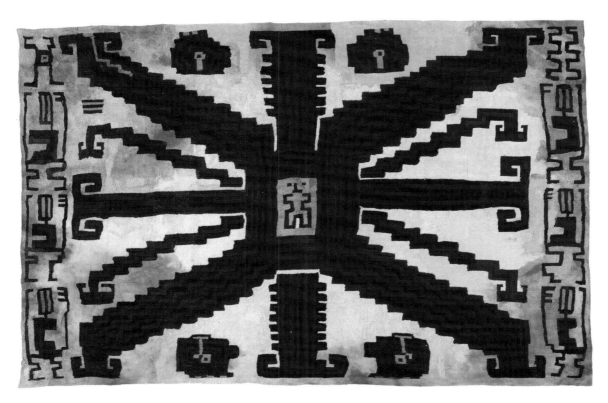

47232

LARGE RECTANGULAR PANEL WITH SCHEMATIC FIGURE AT CENTER

Sihuas
A.D. 100–400
Cotton, camelid fibers
Height 63⅛ in. Width 74⅜ in.

The vertically-oriented small central rectangle contains a schematic standing frontal figure in red, blue, and white on a light buff natural fiber ground. From this, four step-edged rays in indigo and deep red create a dominant X-shaped design. These end in hooks, as do a smaller set of stepped diagonal rays running parallel to and on the center-facing edges of the larger ones. The hooked endings of this secondary set are all four turned to face the textile's bottom edge. A wide central vertical band in alternating red and blue is edged with toothed forms and ends at top and bottom in antenna-like hooks. Thinner, toothless bands create a centered horizontal axis, these also with similar outward-facing end hooks. The four triangular areas reserved top and bottom at either side of the vertical bar have block-like, radically conventionalized profile human heads in indigo and dark red. These face inward, their tops toward the textile top and bottom edges. A natural buff eye and "tear" line complete the images. At either side a relatively narrow band has been reserved, which contains three complete outline-rendered schematic figures, with slightly differing geometric fillers at the top on either side. The figures "face" inward, as indicated both by a raised hand on the inside and a striped tail at the outside. Their C-shaped bodies are oriented in part outwardly and in part inwardly.

The condition is poor. There is extensive replacement and staining of the white ground, especially in the upper right quadrant. While many segments of the primary patterning have patches, a majority of original remaining patterns insures an accurate understanding of the entire design.

Provenance
Westermann Collection, Germany (1950s–70)
Splendors of the World, Haiku, Hawaii

Estimate: $10,000-$15,000

47233

LARGE MANTLE

Sihuas
A.D. 100–400
Camelid fiber, cotton
Height 55 in. Width 76⅞ in.

The design is organized around a large X-shape centered by a rectangle. On a white ground this central rectangle contains a radically stylized human figure with arms and legs forming a disjointed X, the axis of which is perpendicular to that of the large X-shape. All of the linear design extensions progress in steps, which give great vibrancy to the entire surface. The overall mantle rectangle is completed by four pyramidal units in the outer spaces formed by the central X. Two of these, taller and narrower in proportion, have a double-headed serpent motif around an ambiguous central unit. The shallower, broader pyramidal spaces are filled with symmetrically balanced geometric stepped-terrace shapes. The implied overall ground color is white, with the other principal colors being dark hues of a least three shades of blue and two of cochineal red. Small squares of pale gold appear solely in the central motif. The overall condition is fair, with numerous loss areas and some replacement patches.

Provenance
Butterfields, San Francisco: sale 7307E, 25 March 2002, lot 5036, p.11, ill. p.10

Estimate: $10,000-$15,000

47234

TUNIC

Nasca
100 B.C.–A.D. 250
Cotton and camelid fibers
Length 38⅝ in. Width 35⅝ in.

The plain weave cochineal red main body of the tunic is ornamented with an overall tie-dye pattern in lozenges alternating between the natural white fiber color and a now-pale buff. The longer borders are alike in a tightly woven subtle geometric striping, and the shorter borders are knitted. The neck slit is unbound. Considerable wear, especially at the neck and at one side where the arm would have rested, indicates that this tunic was well used in daily life in ancient Peru.

Provenance
Bonhams & Butterfields, San Francisco: sale 7437E, 9 June 2003, lot 5124, p. 33

Estimate: $3,000-$5,000

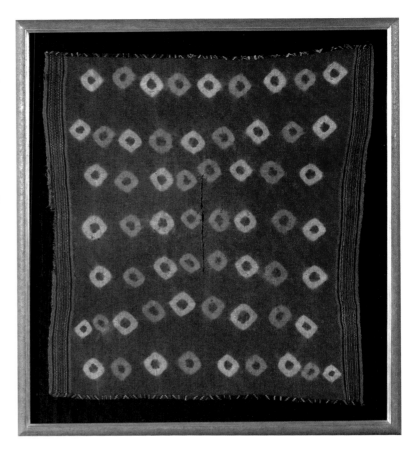

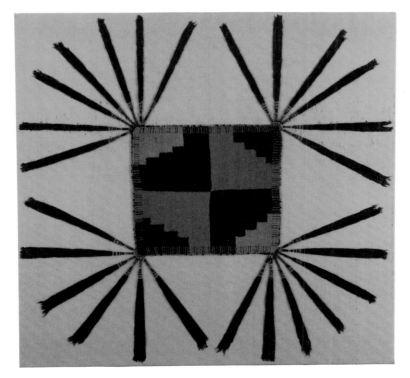

47235

COCA CLOTH WITH CORNER TASSELS

Nasca
100 B.C.–A.D. 200
Camelid fibers
Height (as mounted) 38⅞ in. Width (as mounted) 37½ in.

The carefully knitted and embroidered edging, along with the addition of six beautifully finished tassels at each corner, all suggest that the original purpose of this relatively small textile square was of great importance. The basic square was divided into diagonally symmetrical quadrants, two buff and two dark brown. Each of these has a contrasting stepped corner inset in the same colors. A knitted edging in cochineal red, pale gold, and brown is integrated into the square in the same three colors by closely spaced embroidered lines each punctuated by two loops. These colors also bind and attach the long dark brown corner tassels. The condition is very good with only minor abrasions in the knitted and embroidered areas.

Provenance
Arte Textil (Steve Berger), San Francisco, California

Estimate: $3,000-$4,000

47236

BELT

Nasca
A.D. 100–500
Camelid fibers, cotton
Length 53¾ in. Width 1¾ in.

The design of this almost perfectly preserved belt in slit-tapestry weave is planned in paired units. Each unit is made up of two long rectangles with abutting solid fields of contrasting colors (blue/gold or red/blue) with their inner sides stepped downward to an edge, this edge reversing with each pair. The reserved central portion has six descending stepped bands in contrasting colors, with the addition of black and white bands. Two equally-spaced vertical stripes separate the whole into three segments of two pairs each.

Provenance
Arte Textil (Steve Berger), San Francisco, California

Estimate: $300-$400

47237

HEADBAND

Nasca
A.D. 100–500
Camelid fibers, cotton
Length 144 in. Width 1½ in.

A longer, central narrow band is joined at either end by shorter, wider bands, these finished at their outer ends with a six-inch fringe. The ground color of this textile done in a variation of double-weave is a rich old rose, with the design worked out in the intentionally limited colors of light blue, gold, and white, with black outlining details. The narrow band shows a long parade of conventionalized profile zoomorphs, every other one oriented to an opposite edge. The end bands alternate two more complex units seen frontally or from above. These are formed as developed zoomorphs. Condition is excellent.

Provenance
Arte Textil (Steve Berger), San Francisco, California

Estimate: $1,000-$1,500

47238

SASH WITH BRAIDED STREAMERS

Nasca
100 B.C.–A.D. 250
Cotton, camelid fibers
Height (band) 7⅛ in. Length 27¼ in.
Width (streamers) 3½ in. Length 85 in.

This rather unusual piece is comprised of a wide band assembled from two narrower bands to form a complex, lozenge-based geometric design. At one end of the large band, two braided streamers over eighty inches long have been interwoven with each component part to make a smooth transition from the patterning of the large band. The color range in browns and related neutrals is especially sophisticated. The condition is very good.

Provenance
Bonhams & Butterfields, San Francisco: sale 7437E, 9 June 2003, lot 5135, p.35

Estimate: $2,000-$3,000

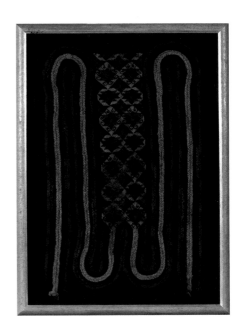

47239

STYLIZED PORTRAIT HEAD
FOR FUNERARY ARRAY

Huari (possibly)
A.D. 500–1000
Gold, silver, cotton and camelid yarns, feathers, gourd
Height 19½ in. Width 8 in. Depth 10½ in.

This is an example of a group of similar such elaborately constructed portrait heads for funerary bundles. All combine segments of feathers on cloth backings, gold and silver, and a variety of woven and plain textiles. The resulting effect is colorfully dramatic.

The face is in orange-red macaw feathers overlaid by a silver-gilt nose in high relief, with flat eye and mouth panels and "tear" streamers flowing from the eyes to the edge of the chin, all in silver-gilt. The eyes are outlined in overlaid black feathers, and there are black feather pupils in red-painted areas representing the whites of the eyes. A horizontal red feather band separates upper and lower lips, behind which are six vertical black sewn bands with some remains of black feathers. A band of alternating blue and red feathers attached to cloth binds the edge of the face, with two silver cutwork circlets at the proper right side. The face is topped by a woven textile band into which hair has been threaded. Over this is laid a tapestry-weave band tied at the back of the head.

The headdress is based on a gourd core around which is a red fabric roll (possibly modern) over which is bound a varicolored feather-on-fiber band. Ten circumference holes have been punctured around a central hole in the gourd. In these a central and seven circumference orange-red macaw tail feathers remain, all topped by tufts of blue and black feathers laid into salmon-colored feathers. Each of these vertical assemblages had two silver disks added, some of which remain.

The present condition manifests expected feather loss and breakage. Some of the textiles are faded or stained. There is some stabilization and reattachment with modern white thread.

Provenance
William Siegal Galleries, Santa Fe: 2004 catalogue, item 26
Bentley Dillard Collection, Scottsdale

Published
Siegal, William. *Pre-Columbian Art*. Santa Fe: William Siegal Galleries, 2004.

Estimate: $10,000-$15,000

47240

TUNIC PANEL

Huari
A.D. 600–900
Feathers sewn to cloth backing
Height 24¾ in. Width 30¾ in.

This bold image formed either the front or back of a tunic. The loosely woven textile base is completely covered by the feather design, executed primarily in macaw and parrot feathers. The focal motif on the blue ground is a yellow, eight-rayed face with large staring eyes and bared teeth. Salmon-orange feathers outline this central "sun," frame the eyes, and suggest a tongue between the rows of teeth. Four squares in the same salmon-orange frame the rayed image, and two similarly colored rectangular tabs connect with the outer edges just above the half-way point. Other than a normal amount of feather loss, the condition is good.

Provenance
Dr. Wally and Brenda Zollman Collection, Indianapolis
Dylan Graeme Collection
Butterfields, San Francisco: sale 7307E, 25 March 2002, lot 5075, p.24, ill. p.24

Publications
José Antonio DeLavalle, *Arte y Tesoros del Peru*. Lima: Banco de Credito del Peru en la Cultura, 1984, #115 (illustrated).
Edward H. Merrin and Linda Schildkraut. *Precolumbian Masterpieces: Mexico, Peru, Central America, American Indian.* New York: Edward H. Merrin, 1985, #26 (illustrated).
Lee A. Parsons, John B. Carlson & Peter David Joralemon, *The Face of Ancient America,* Indianapolis: Indianapolis Museum of Art, 1988, pp.216-217, #153 (illustrated).

Estimate: $10,000-$15,000

47241

FEATHER-COVERED BAND FOR CEREMONIAL ATTIRE

Nasca (?)
A.D. 100–300
Macaw feathers on textile
Height 5½ in. Diameter (as mounted) 8⅛ in.

A large amount of featherwork comes from South Coast burials and is usually designated Nasca. Blue feathers from the blue-and-yellow macaw have been sewn to a long, rather loosely-woven brown textile band. Such bands formed parts of high-status dress. The band is in good condition.

Provenance
Bonhams & Butterfields, San Francisco: sale 7477E, 8 December 2003, lot 3066, pp.20-21 (there mounted with a gold diadem and pectoral being offered as a separate lot in the present sale)

Estimate: $5,000-$7,000

47242

TUNIC PANEL

Chimú
A.D. 1100–1400
Camelid fibers, cotton
Height 69¼ in. Width 14 in.

This red-ground tapestry-weave tunic panel shows nine pairs of frontally displayed human figures standing under angled arches and flanked by rampant monkeys. When folded for wearing, all figures were seen in upright orientation. The furry areas of the monkeys are represented by small, closely spaced loops which create a strong illusion of shaggy coats and add a rarely seen third dimension to this textile. Principal colors used are two tones of natural brown for the monkeys and white, two shades of gold, light blue, muted green, and dark cochineal burgundy for the human figures. The usual varied color distributions include cross alternations of white in most of the arches, which creates a zig-zagging effect. At one end the weaver misjudged spacing and had to compress two rows of figures. Although the condition is generally good, there is loss in some of the looped areas.

Provenance
Bonhams & Butterfields, San Francisco: sale 7477E, 8 December 2003, lot 3080, p.26

Estimate: $5,000-$6,000

47243

THREE TEMPLE PANELS FROM WALL HANGING ENSEMBLE

Chimú (Early)
A.D. 1000–1100
Cotton; warp ikat
(A) Height 118⅜ in. Width 22¾ in.
(B) Height 115 in.   Width 46¾ in.
(C) Height 105 in.   Width 46½ in.

Warp ikat textiles are rare among pre-conquest Peruvian examples. According to a verbal statement to the source by Nobuko Kajitani, these examples most likely originated in the Lambayeque area relatively early in the period of Chimú dominance. The ikat technique, as used here, has resulted in subtle, nuanced design and color harmonies. The resulting shapes are more difficult to read, but in part can be seen as groupings of birds in various configurations. The larger-scaled intermittent bands both unify the design and create a repeated pulsation across the surface. Large-sized groups of like textiles served as temple hangings, probably in some cases in the huge outdoor courts where thousands of people were assembled. There are a few repaired small losses, with the overall condition good.

Provenance
Westermann Collection, Germany (1955–1970)
Splendors of the World, Haiku, Hawaii

Estimate: $30,000-$40,000

47244

PAINTED PANEL

Chimú
A.D. 1100–1400
Cotton fibers, brown pigment
Length 54⅛ in. Width 15⅜ in.

The preserved section represents parts of two loom widths joined before painting. Selvages remain on both shorter sides and one longer. The design is organized in alternating wider and narrower bands horizontally across the joined widths. Nine units survive, these so arranged that a rayed frontal face on a white circular ground forms intermittent diagonals which move across the field. Other motif repetitions are similarly staggered diagonally, but their execution in fine pale lines against a uniform brown lessens their pulsation quality. Motifs include birds, fish, animals, and humans, all in consistently whimsical stylizations. The remaining portion is in good overall condition, with a few areas of loss along the cut side.

Provenance
Bonhams & Butterfields, San Francisco: sale 7477E, 8 December 2003, lot 3090, p.31, ill. p.30

Estimate: $2,000-$3,000

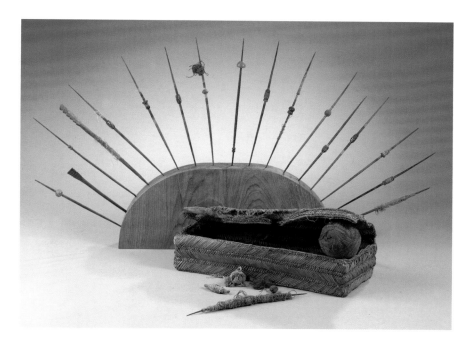

47245

WEAVER'S KIT IN A LIDDED BASKET

Chimú
A.D. 1100–1400
Plant fiber; wood, ceramic
Pigment; camelid and cotton fibers
Maximum basket height 5 in., width 6 in.,
length 14¾ in.

This is an example of what must have been a standard size and shape basketry container for a weaver's kit. The contents presently include a spindle with twine, a whorl with two skeins of thread, a large medium brown ball of yarn, several skeins of different colored threads, and some miscellaneous weaving-related objects. A group of fourteen spindles with whorls has been removed by the owner and are displayed in a teak mount. The basket is worn from daily use by the ancient weaver as well as by time. The basket contents vary in condition, while thirteen of the mounted spindles with whorls are in good condition. The remaining spindle has a cracked and bent lower section to the spindle.

Provenance
Skinner, Boston: sale 2209, 20 September 2003

Estimate: $500-$800

47246

PILE WEAVE BAND ("JAGUAR TAIL" COSTUME COMPONENT)

Middle Horizon, Huari-related (?)
A.D. 500–800
Camelid fibers, cotton
Length 20½ in. Width 5⁷⁄₁₆ in.

The uncertain period and cultural attribution for this unusual piece is based on its weaving technique, which was developed at Tiwanaku and flourished under the expansionist Huari. The three-dimensional pile texture, the irregular shape, and the patterning of this textile inevitably suggest the tail section of a jaguar pelt. Since it is finished and bordered all around, the textile constitutes a complete unit. This suggests that it may have been a component of a costume.The pile-textured "pelt" has an off-white ground with two colors of rich brown forming the pelage. A few small accents of old rose connect this center portion harmoniously with the old rose bordering band. Other than a few minor frayed spots, the condition is very good.

Provenance
Bonhams & Butterfields, San Francisco: sale 7437E, 9 June 2003, lot 5123, p.33

Estimate: $1,200-$1,800

47247

GROUP OF SIX STANDING FIGURES ON A PILLOW

Chancay
A.D. 1000–1350
Cotton and camelid fibers; Sticks
Height 15 in. Width 21¾ in. Depth 18¾ in.

Such groups of figures made of textiles arranged on a rudimentary reed framework and placed on pillow-like bases have been found in large numbers in the Peruvian Central Coast burial sites commonly designated as Chancay. Many appear to enact episodes from daily and ceremonial life. A further difficulty is the uncertainty whether or not most of those which reach North American collections were actually found in the groupings in which they are now exhibited. (A remarkable collection, which has a good chance of being as found, is held in the non-public section of the Amano Museum in Lima.) All of the visible components in this grouping are ancient and the overall condition is good for their age.

Provenance
Bentley Dillard, Scottsdale, Arizona
William Siegal Galleries, Santa Fe: 2004 catalogue, item 36 (illustrated).

Published
Siegal, William. *Pre-Columbian Art*. Santa Fe: William Siegal Galleries, 2004.

Estimate: $6,000-$8,000

47248

RECTANGULAR CHECKERBOARD PANEL

Nasca
100 B.C.–A.D. 300
Camelid fibers
Length 62 in. Width 42½ in.

Large textile panels made up of bold, strongly-colored rectangular units could have had a number of uses. In addition to being worn or used for carrying, they might have formed components in wall hangings. With the muted colors of both the coastal landscape and regional building materials, colorful textiles would have been a primary vivifying element for Nasca daily life. There are scattered losses in some rectangles.

Provenance
Splendors of the World, Haiku, Hawaii

Estimate: $8,000-$12,000

47249

TUNIC

Nasca
200 B.C.–A.D. 400
Camelid, cotton fibers
Length 48 in. Width 36 in.

When worn, this now opened tunic showed two major design units from each view. Based visually on a rather steep-sided stepped pyramidal shape, the rows of four colors move at a slight diagonal across the loom widths. This produces a design that tilts as it moves out at the fringed lower edges. The colors are a deep cochineal red and three natural tones of dark brown, medium brown, and buff. The loosely woven textile is in moderately good condition, with some staining.

Provenance
Bonhams & Butterfields, San Francisco: sale 7477E, 8 December 2003, p. 32, ill. p.32

Estimate: $2,500-$3,000

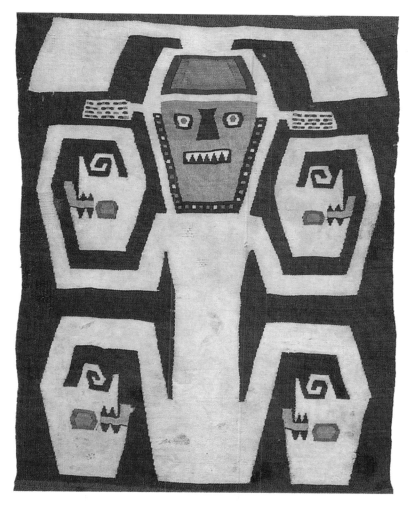

47250

LARGE TEMPLE TEXTILE PANEL WITH THREE STYLIZED FIGURES

Ica
A.D. 1000–1350
Camelid Fiber, and cotton
Height 93¼ in. Width 22¾ in.

The large size and bold scale of this interlocked tapestry-weave textile suggest that it was for a public context. It could have been a segment of a still larger temple hanging, or it might have functioned as a public banner. The red-ground continuously woven field shows three large white crescent-crowned frontally displayed figures placed one on top of the other. The staring-eyed faces have bared teeth and the hands and feet are transformed into simplified monstrous heads in profile. Face and head details are in a muted gold almost identical to the integrally woven bottom and top border bands which depict processions of red birds, again in profile. Other than minor losses and stains, the condition is good.

Provenance
Arte Textil (Steve Berger), San Francisco, California

Estimate: $12,000-$15,000

47251

CHECKERBOARD TUNIC

Inca
A.D. 1450–1530
Camelid fibers, cotton
Height (at center as mounted) 32½ in. Width (at top as mounted) 28½ in.

Tunics in red, black, and white arranged in this checkerboard design have survived in sufficient numbers to support the interpretation that they served as some kind of military uniform. As Rebecca Stone-Miller (*Art of the Andes from Chavín to Inca*. New York: Thames and Hudson, 1995, p.212) notes, "Clothing was an instrument of conformity, unmistakably signaling imperial power. Imagine 10,000 warriors in checkerboard tunics advancing over the hill!" This example is in the standard tight, close tapestry weave characteristic of Inca textiles. The neck, armholes, and lower edge have an embroidered binding. The present military tunic has extensive overall wear, stains, and creases.

Provenance
Arte Textil (Steve Berger), San Francisco, California

Estimate: $4,000-$5,000

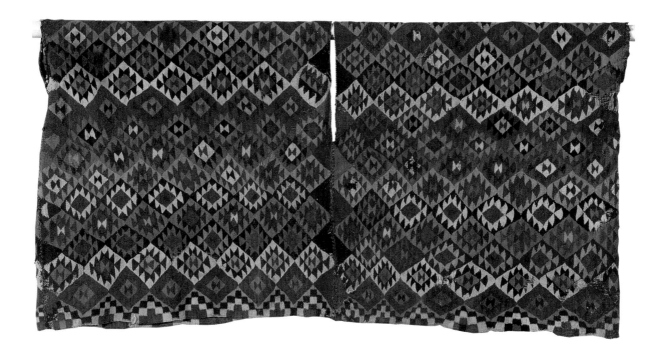

47252

TUNIC

Inca-Chimú
A.D. 1100–1400
Camelid fiber, cotton
Height 22¼ in (as mounted) Width 48 in. (at bottom as mounted)
Wearer's Left panel front (at sleeve): Width 20 in. Length 45 in.
Wearer's Right panel front (at sleeve): Width 20 in. Length 44⅜ in.

The overall design of this colorful tunic is based
on a lozenge which has interior units of varying
combinations formed by triangles. These lozenge
units are ordered in horizontal bands of shared
ground colors. As the tunic would have been seen on
a wearer, three evenly spaced horizontal bands have
white as a prevalent color, thus creating a pulsating
visual subdivision of the front. A slightly differing
half-lozenge band at the bottom stabilizes the design.
Condition of one side is good, while the other has
several areas of abrasion and fiber loss.

Provenance
David Bernstein, New York

Estimate: $3,000-$5,000

47253

***TOCAPU* TUNIC**

Inca
A.D. 1450–1530
Camelid fibers, cotton
Height 23¼ in. Width (at top) 26¼ in.

Woven in the tightest, imperial quality tapestry weave, this *tocapu* tunic has on each side, as seen when worn, a major top field of identically-sized squares in over ten different designs. These are arranged in six horizontal bands of ten squares across each (for the entire tunic this totals one-hundred twenty squares). Below the main field, a single band the width of two square rows has a continuous design of connected hexagons containing and surrounded by rows of small linked triangles. A narrow dark brown plain band at bottom is bound with a multi-colored embroidered edging.

Tocapu textiles were the prerogative of members of the Inca imperial clan and higher level elite individuals. The extensively varied patterns which appear in the squares are thought to have encoded information conveying rank and privileges of the individuals wearing these garments, as well as indication that they controlled a variety of ethnicities within the empire (Rebecca Stone-Miller. *Art of the Andes from Chavín to Inca.* New York: Thames and Hudson, 1995, p. 210). Certain of these patterns occur as the overall single motif of a tunic which would have been worn by a lower status individual.

The visible side of the tunic as displayed has abrasions and stains concentrated at the neck slit and armhole areas, indicating that the tunic was worn in daily ceremonial life. The non-visible side has a larger number of abrasions and losses, as does the dark lower border all around the tunic.

Provenance
Arte Textil (Steve Berger), San Francisco, California

Estimate: $18,000-$24,000

47254

QUIPU

Inca
A.D. 1430–1530
Cotton, camelid fibers
Diameter 34½ in. at break-point

The present example has been disentangled and mounted in the standard circular format. It illustrates a range of cord colors and knotting patterns, the method developed by the Inca administration to record the remarkably accurate census, tax, and resource information which was central to the efficiency and effective extension of the Inca empire. The condition is good.

Provenance
Splendors of the World, Haiku, Hawaii

Estimate: $2,500-$3,500

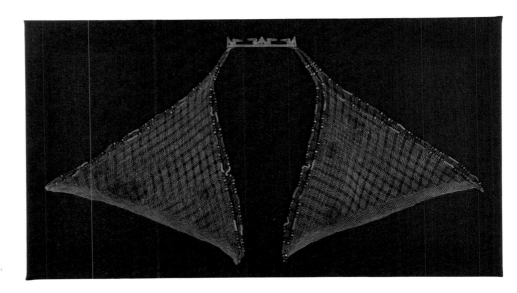

47255

SCALE ASSEMBLAGE

Inca
A.D. 1430–1530
Balance Bar: Metal Alloy (Silvered)
Weighing Baskets: Cotton and Camelid fibers
Height 22⅛ in. (as mounted) Width 41 in. (as mounted)

Comprised of a silvered metal alloy
balance bar and a pair of triangular netted fiber weighing bags, the assemblage is mounted flat on a fabric backing. The long rectangular balance bar has pairs of sitting long-beaked birds facing one another from center and end positions. The netting weighing bags are edged in tubular knitted bands in red, gold, black, and white. The bar is in excellent condition, while the bags show areas of loss and wear. Without information on find conditions, it is impossible to know whether or not the components were originally together.

Provenance
Splendors of the World, Haiku, Hawaii

Estimate: $1,500-$2,500

47256

AYMARA / CHUA PONCHO

Peru
ca. A.D. 1875
Cotton and Alpaca fibers
Length (open) 43 in. Width 38 in.

This tunic originated from the Puno section of Peru very close to Lake Titicaca. It was woven using a warp face technique with camelid and cotton fibers by a member of the Aymara culture living near Chua. The large black mid section is banded by red, white, and indigo striping. The condition is very good, with some minor staining.

Provenance
Collected 1981 in La Paz, Bolivia by Steve Berger and Roger Yorke
Arte Textil (Steve Berger), San Francisco

Estimate: $1,200-$1,800

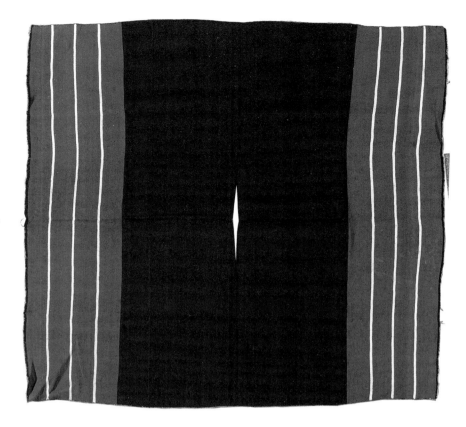

47257

COCA CLOTH TEXTILE

Jihuacota Region, Province of Ingavi, Department of La Paz, Bolivia
ca. A.D. 1875
Cotton, camelid fibers
Length 32 in. Width 31 in.

This banded textile is a Jihuacota *tari*, or coca cloth for use in Aymara women's ritual ceremonies as a ground cover or a coca leaf wrap. It is woven in a striped pattern using natural dyes of brown, red, gray, purple, blue, and green. The knitted binding of red, white, and blue fibers finishes all edges. Cotton and camelid fibers, or fibers from soft tree bark, are traditionally woven in a square format using a warp face technique. The condition is very good.

Provenance
Collected 1981 in La Paz, Bolivia, by Steve Berger and Roger Yorke
Arte Textil (Steve Berger), San Francisco

Estimate: $800-$1,000

47258

TUNIC

Late Horizon or Early Spanish-Colonial
A.D. 1400–1600
Camelid and cotton fibers
Length 58 in. Width 48 in.

The principal color of this tunic is a deep cochineal red. Set symmetrically to each side at the position of the outer torso limits are bands of four contiguous units of narrow vertical stripes in green, dusky pink, dark blue, and the same deep cochineal red. Beyond these at each side is a wider band of natural brown followed by an equal-sized band of the cochineal red. A narrow green band terminates each edge. Woven into this principal tunic body at the bottom borders is a continuous five-and-one-half inch wide band of alternating seven-eighths inch vertical stripes of natural dark brown and white. This ends in a single horizontal small-scale chevron band of the same two colors with its points moving from the outer edge to meet at the center. Below this is a brown and white fringe of roughly thirteen-and-one-half inches, each change of color marked by a twisted fringe element combining brown and white. The condition generally is good, with a few losses and minor staining.

Provenance
Arte Textil (Steve Berger), San Francisco, California

Estimate: $3,000-$4,000

47259

TWO COCA BAGS WITH EXTENSIVE FRINGE

Late Horizon
A.D. 1300–1530
Camelid fibers, cotton
Height 23⅜ in. Width 12 in.

These similar rectangular fringed coca bags are patterned in bands of muted color oriented to the longer axis. Many of the bands have woven, conventionalized pictographic designs of birds and reptiles. In each example it is uncertain whether or not the extended fringe arranged as horizontal stripes and bound in small units is original to the pouch. The smaller pouch has more wear and abrasion than the large example. In both the long fringe is in good condition.

Provenance
Bonhams & Butterfields, San Francisco: sale 7437E, 9 June 2003, lot 5123, p.33

Estimate: $2,000-$3,000

End of Pre-Columbian Art Session

GLOSSARY

Addorsed—Presented back-to-back, often connected or in close proximity.

Agnathic—Lacking jaws or with poorly formed jaws.

Amacalli—Nahuatl, literally "house of paper"; the pleated paper fan which was a part of head accoutrements of several deities and was also incorporated into headdresses of costumed deity impersonators.

Atlatl—The word for spear-thrower in Nahuatl, the language spoken by the Aztec of Central Mexico. Medium-length darts were set in a notch near the end of the atlatl, the user grasped the other end, using the thumb hook to steady his grip. The extra resulting arm extension greatly increased length and power of the throw.

Cochineal—A red dye made from the dried and pulverized bodies of the females of a tropical American scale insect (*Dactylopius coccus*) that feeds on certain species of cacti.

Depletion gilding—The use of acid substances to remove the copper from the outer surfaces of alloyed metals which leaves a layer of gold that was then compacted by burnishing. The resulting gold surface is almost invulnerable to corrosion, but through time corrosion of the copper-heavy interior can push through, flaking off the gold and leaving a black powdery substance.

Pepino—A melon-like member of the nightshade family (genus *Solanum*) which was a widely used food in ancient Peru.

Poporo—A term prevalent in Colombia for a container for mineral lime used as a catalyst when chewing coca leaves

Qero—A relatively tall drinking cup developed in pre-Inca times which was widely used in ancient Peru and was continued by the Inca and from them into colonial times.

Quipu—A knotted string device for recording information, developed by the Inca. The use of the *quipu* to record censuses, tax records, and complex organizational information was a key component in the remarkable political and strategic success of the Inca.

Tocapu—In Inca textiles, *Tocapu* were the often complex designs that were reserved for the highest levels of the elite.

Tumbaga—An alloy of copper and gold used frequently in Colombia and lower Central America. The surface was usually treated by depletion gilding to give surface prominence to the gold content.

Tumi—An Andean knife form in which the cutting area is in the shape of a half-circle, out of the flat top of which rises a thick, long-rectangular extension of the same thin planar nature as the blade.

Tunjo—A class of relatively flat, usually hastily cast metal objects, most often in low-grade gold or *tumbaga* which were used as votive offerings by the ancient peoples of the high Andean region around modern-day Bogotá (the Muisca culture). Very specific detail as to objects held and sex of the figure appear to have been functionally important.

Way (pl. *wayob*)—As deciphered independently from each other by Stephen Houston, David Stuart, and Nikolai Grube: "Shaman, Sorcerer, transformation, nagual, animal companion spirit" (Grube and Nahm, 1994, p.686).

BIBLIOGRAPHY

Adelson, Laurie, Arthur Tracht. *Aymara Weavings: Ceremonial Textiles of Colonial and 19th Century Bolivia*, Washington,D.C.: Smithsonian Institution Traveling Exhibition Service, 1983.

Aguilar Piedra, Carlos Humberto. *Los Usékares de Oro*. San José, Costa Rica: Fundación Museos Banco Central, 1996.

Baquedano,Elizabeth. *Aztec Scuplture*. London: British Museum Publications, 1984.

Bonavia, Duccio. *Arte e Historia del Peru Antiguo. Colección Enrico Poli Bianchi*. Arequipa, Peru: Banco del Sur, 1994.

Burger, Richard L. *Chavín and the Origins of the Andean Civilization*. New York: Thames and Hudson Limited, 1995.

Berrin, Kathleen and Esther Pasztory, eds. *Teotihuacan Art from the City of the Gods*. London: Thames and Hudson, 1993.

Bray, Warwick. *The Gold of El Dorado*. London: Times Newspapers Limited, 1978.

Brinckerhoff, Deborah. *A Cosmic View: Pre-Columbian Art From the John Platt Collection*. Greenwich, Connecticut: Bruce Museum, Inc., 1994.

Cardale de Schrimpff, Marianne and Theres Gähwiler-Walder. *Calima Colombie précolombienne*. Martigny, Suisse: Fondation Pierre Gianadda, 1991.

Calvo Mora, Marlin, Leidy Bonilla Vargas, and Julio Sánchez Pérez. *Gold, Jade, Forests / Oro, Jade, Bosques COSTA RICA*. Seattle: University of Washington Press, 1997.

Coe, Michael D. *The Jaguar's Children: Pre-Classic Central Mexico*. New York: The Museum of Primitive Art, 1965.

Crespo Toral, Hernán and Olaf Holm. *Arte Precolombino de Ecuador*. Quito: Salvat Editores Ecuatoriana S.A. 1977.

D'Harcourt, Raoul. *Textiles of Ancient Peru and Their Techniques*. Seattle: University of Washington Press, 1962.

Donnan, Christopher B. *Ceramics of Ancient Peru*. Los Angeles: University of California, 1992.

Falchetti,Ana María. *El Oro del Gran Zenú*. Bogotá: Banco de la República, Museo del Oro, 1995.

Fernández Esquivel, Patricia. *Oro Precolombino de Costa Rica*. San José, Costa Rica: Fundación Museos Banco Central de Costa Rica, 2004.

Grube, Nikolai and Werner Nahm, "A Census of Xibalba: A Complete Inventory of *Way* Characters on Maya Ceramics" in Justin Kerr, *The Maya Vase Book, Volume 4*. New York: Kerr Associates, 1994.

Jones, Julie. *The Art of Precolumbian Gold, The Jan Mitchell Collection*. Boston: Little, Brown and Company, 1985.

Jones, Julie and Heidi King. *Gold of the Americas*. New York: The Metropolitan Museum of Art, 2002.

Labbé, Armand J. *Shamans, Gods, and Mythic Beasts: Colombian Gold and Ceramics in Antiquity*. New York: The American Federation of Arts, 1998.

Lapiner, Alan. *Pre-Columbian Art of South America*. New York: Harry N. Abrams, Inc.,1976.

Lumbreras, Luis G. *The Peoples and Cultures of Ancient Peru*. Washington, D.C.: Smithsonian Institution Press, 1974.

McEwan, Colin, ed. *Precolumbian Gold Technology, Style and Iconography*. Chicago: Fitzroy Dearborn Publishers, 2000.

Museo del Oro. Bogotá: Banco de la Republica, 1968.

Pasztory, Esther. *Aztec Art*. New York: Harry N. Abrams, Inc., 1983.

Reents-Budet, Dorie. *Painting the Maya Universe: Royal Ceramics of the Classic Period*. Durham and London: Duke University Press, 1994.

Reichel-Dolmatoff, Gerardo. *Goldwork and Shamanism*. Medellín: Compañía Litográfica Nacional S.A., 1988.

Reid, James. "Rare Excitement, Marvelous Reality", *Tribal*:VIII: 1- number 30, Spring, 2003 (pp.56–63). San Francisco: Primedia Inc., 2003.

Rowe, Ann Pollard. *Costumes and Featherwork of the Lords of Chimor*. Washington, D.C.: The Textile Museum, 1984.

Rowe, Ann Pollard. *Warp-Patterned Weaves of the Andes*. Washington, D.C.: The Textile Museum, 1977.

Rowe, John Howland. "Standardization in Inca Tapestry Tunics" in Rowe, Ann Pollard, Elizabeth P. Benson, and Anne-Louise Schaffer, eds. *The Junius B. Bird Pre-Columbian Textile Conference*. Washington, D.C.: The Textile Museum and Dumbarton Oaks, 1973.

Santa Barbara Museum of Art. *Diverse Directions. A Collector's Choice. Selections from the Charles Craig Collection*. Santa Barbara: Santa Barbara Museum of Art, 1987.

Stanish, Charles. *Ancient Titicaca. The Evolution of Complex Society in Southern Peru and Northern Bolivia*. Berkley: University of California Press, 2003.

Stone-Miller, Rebecca. *Art of the Andes from Chavín to Inca*. New York: Thames and Hudson, 1995.

Stone-Miller, Rebecca. *To Weave for the Sun*. New York: Thames and Hudson, 1992.

Tushingham, A.D. *Gold for the Gods*. Toronto: Royal Ontario Museum, 1976.

von Winning, Hasso. *The John-Platt Collection of Pre-Columbian Art*. Charlottesville, Virginia: The University of Virginia Art Museum, 1986.

Young-Sánchez, Margaret. *Tiwanaku. Ancestors of the Inca*. Lincoln and London: University of Nebraska Press for Denver Art Museum, 2004.

DECORATIVE ART AUCTION

October 20-21, 2006 • Dallas, Texas • Live and Online

Important, exquisitely carved ivory figure of Louis XVI regally posed next to his crown, all set on a wood plinth complete with ivory fleur-de-lys, rosettes, and two cartouches signifying the duration of his reign

French, 19th Century
21 1/8 in. overall height
Estimate $5,000–8,000

To receive a complimentary catalogue or book of your choice, simply register online at HA.com/Join. Enter Reference #5116.

Annual Sales Exceeding $500 Million • Over 250,000 Registered Online Bidder-Members

THE INTELLIGENT ALTERNATIVE
HERITAGE
Auction Galleries

3500 Maple Ave, 17th Floor • Dallas, Texas 75219 • 214-443-8444 • 800-872-6467 ext. 444 • HA.com/FineArt

Auctioneer John Petty. TX License #00013740 • This auction is subject to a 19.5% Buyer's Premium

5116

HERITAGE

IMPORTANT FINE ART AUCTION

November 9-10, 2006 • Dallas, Texas • Live and Online

Maxfield Parrish
Poet's Dream, 1901
Oil on panel
Private Collection
Photo from the archives of Alma Gilbert; used with permission.

To receive a complimentary catalogue or book of your choice,
simply register online at HA.com/Join. Enter Reference #5116.

Annual Sales Exceeding $500 Million • Over 250,000 Registered Online Bidder-Members

3500 Maple Ave, 17th Floor • Dallas, Texas 75219 • 214-443-8444 • 800-872-6467 ext. 444 • HA.com/FineArt

Auctioneer John Petty. TX License #00013740 • This auction is subject to a 19.5% Buyer's Premium

THE INTELLIGENT ALTERNATIVE

HERITAGE
Auction Galleries

5116

HERITAGE
IMPORTANT FINE ART AUCTION
November 9-10, 2006 • Dallas, Texas • Live and Online

Peter Paul Rubens (Flemish 1577–1640)
Allegory of the Spanish Monarchy (Fortitude), ca. 1630, private collection

To receive a complimentary catalogue or book of your choice,
simply register online at HA.com/Join. Enter Reference #5116.

Annual Sales Exceeding $500 Million • Over 250,000 Registered Online Bidder-Members

3500 Maple Ave, 17th Floor • Dallas, Texas 75219 • 214-443-8444 • 800-872-6467 ext. 444 • HA.com/FineArt

Auctioneer John Petty. TX License #00013740 • This auction is subject to a 19.5% Buyer's Premium

THE INTELLIGENT ALTERNATIVE
HERITAGE
Auction Galleries

5116

HERITAGE
EARLY TEXAS ART AUCTION

December 2, 2006 • Dallas, Texas • Live and Online

Robert William Wood, *Floral Spectrum*, 29 x 43 in. (Detail)

To receive a complimentary catalogue or book of your choice, simply register online at HA.com/Join. Enter Reference #5116.

Annual Sales Exceeding $500 Million • Over 250,000 Registered Online Bidder Members

3500 Maple Ave, 17th Floor • Dallas, Texas 75219 • 214-443-8444 ■ 800-872-6467 ext. 444 • HA.com/FineArt

THE INTELLIGENT ALTERNATIVE
HERITAGE
Auction Galleries

Auctioneer John Petty. TX License #00013740 • This auction is subject to a 19.5% Buyer's Premium

5116

HERITAGE

SIGNATURE JEWELRY AND TIMEPIECES

December 6, 2006 • Dallas, Texas • Live and Online

WE INVITE YOU TO CONSIGN
to our Winter 2006 Jewelry & Timepieces Signature Auction.

Deadline: September 29, 2006

Contact Jill Burgum at 800-872-6467 ext. 697 to be a part of history as we celebrate the past, present, and future of fine jewelry and timepieces.

To receive a complimentary catalogue or book of your choice, simply register online at HA.com/Join. Enter Reference #5116.

Annual Sales Exceeding $500 Million • Over 250,000 Registered Online Bidder-Members

3500 Maple Ave, 17th Floor • Dallas, Texas 75219 • 214-443-8444 • 800-872-6467 ext. 444 • HA.com/Jewelry

Auctioneer John Petty. TX License #00013740 • This auction is subject to a 19.5% Buyer's Premium

THE INTELLIGENT ALTERNATIVE

HERITAGE
Auction Galleries

5116

HERITAGE

AFRICAN AND OCEANIC ART AUCTION

December 7-8, 2006 • Dallas, Texas • Live and Online

WE INVITE YOU TO CONSIGN
CONSIGNMENT DEADLINE:
OCTOBER 16

- GENEROUS CASH ADVANCES AVAILABLE
- COMPETITIVE CONSIGNMENT TERMS
- TIMELY PAYMENT TO CONSIGNORS SINCE 1976

An exceptionally fine Baga effigy drum, Guinea

To receive a complimentary catalogue or book of your choice,
simply register online at HA.com/Join. Enter Reference #5116.

Annual Sales Exceeding $500 Million • Over 250,000 Registered Online Bidder-Members

3500 Maple Ave, 17th Floor • Dallas, Texas 75219 • 214-443-8444 • 800-872-6467 ext. 444 • HA.com/FineArt

Auctioneer John Petty. TX License #00013740 • This auction is subject to a 19.5% Buyer's Premium

THE INTELLIGENT ALTERNATIVE
HERITAGE
Auction Galleries

511

HERITAGE AUCTION GALLERIES – UPCOMING AUCTIONS

Fine & Decorative Arts	Location	Auction Dates	Consignment Deadline
Decorative Art Signature Auction	Dallas, TX	October 20-21, 2006	August 29, 2006
Fine Art, Platinum & Signature Auctions	Dallas, TX	November 9-10, 2006	September 19, 2006
Texas Art Signature Auction	Dallas, TX	December 2, 2006	October 10, 2006
African & Oceanic Art Signature Auction	Dallas, TX	December 7-8, 2006	October 16, 2006
Jewelry and Timepieces	**Location**	**Auction Dates**	**Consignment Deadline**
Estate Jewelry and Timepeices	Dallas, TX	December 6, 2006	September 29, 2006
Vintage Movie Posters	**Location**	**Auction Dates**	**Consignment Deadline**
Dallas Signature Auction	Dallas, TX	November 14, 2006	September 22, 2006
United States Coins	**Location**	**Auction Dates**	**Consignment Deadline**
Denver Signature & Platinum Night Auction	Denver, CO	August 13-14, 2006	Closed
Long Beach Signature Auction	Long Beach, CA	September 13-16, 2006	August 3, 2006
Dallas Signature Auction	Dallas, TX	October 24–26, 2006	September 12, 2006
Dallas Signature Auction	Dallas, TX	November 29–30, 2006	October 17, 2006
World Coins	**Location**	**Auction Dates**	**Consignment Deadline**
Long Beach Signature Auction	Long Beach, CA	September 14-15, 2006	July 26, 2006
Currency	**Location**	**Auction Dates**	**Consignment Deadline**
Long Beach Signature Auction	Long Beach, CA	September 14-15, 2006	July 26, 2006
Comics	**Location**	**Auction Dates**	**Consignment Deadline**
Dallas Signature Auction	Dallas, TX	August 10-12, 2006	Closed
Baltimore Signature Auction	Baltimore, MD	September 8-9, 2006	July 27, 2006
Dallas Signature Auction	Dallas, TX	November 16-18, 2006	October 5, 2006
Music & Entertainment Memorabilia	**Location**	**Auction Dates**	**Consignment Deadline**
Dallas Signature Auction	Dallas, TX	October 6-7, 2006	August 15, 2006
Political Memorabilia & Americana	**Location**	**Auction Dates**	**Consignment Deadline**
Grand Format Autographs Auction (NYC Simulcast)	Dallas, TX	October 12, 2006	August 21, 2006
Political Memorabilia & Americana Signature Auction	Dallas, TX	December 13, 2006	October 18, 2006
Sports Collectibles	**Location**	**Auction Dates**	**Consignment Deadline**
Dallas Signature Auction	Dallas, TX	October 28, 2006	September 5, 2006

HERITAGE WEEKLY INTERNET COIN AUCTIONS
New Auctions begin every
Tuesday and Friday at 10 PM CT.

HERITAGE WEEKLY INTERNET CURRENCY AUCTIONS
Close, and a new one begins, every
Tuesday at 10 PM CT.

HERITAGE WEEKLY INTERNET COMICS AUCTIONS
Close, and a new one begins, every
Sunday of each month at 10 PM CT.

HERITAGE MONTHLY MARKETPLACE AUCTIONS
Use a unique format wherein all lots close in
succession rather than all at once, on Wednesdays/
Thursdays between 4 PM and 10 PM CT. This
Auction has a combination of lots consisting of
Americana, Sports, Comics, Fine Art/Decorative
Arts, Texas Art and Music Memorabilia.

HERITAGE WEEKLY INTERNET MOVIE POSTER AUCTIONS
Begin and end every
Sunday at 10 PM CT.

HERITAGE MONTHLY INTERNET SPORTS AUCTIONS
Close, and a new one begins, on the last
Sunday of each month at 10 PM CT.

HA.com
Call Our Consignment Hotline Toll Free:
800-872-6467 Ext. 222 (24-hour VM)

HERITAGE
Auction Galleries
Over 250,000 Online Registered Bidder-Members
Annual Sales Exceeding $500 Million

Heritage Numismatic Auctions, Inc.: California 3S 3062 16 63, Florida AB0000665, Ohio 2006000050. Currency Auctions of America: Florida AB 2218. Auctioneers: Leo Frese: Florida AU 0001059. California 3S 3062 16 64, NewYork City; Day 1094965, Night 1094966; Samuel Foose: Texas 00011727, California 3S 3062 16 65, Florida AU3244, Ohio 2006000048, and New York City; Day 0952360, Night 0952361. Jim Fitzgerald: Texas Associate 16130. Mike Sadler: Texas Associate 16129. Scott Peterson: Texas 00013256, Florida AU3021. Robert Korver: Ohio 2006000049, Texas 13754, and New York City; Day 1096338 and Night 1096340.

7/19/06

NEW YORK STATE AUCTIONS ONLY

These Terms and Conditions of Sale are designed to conform to the applicable sections of the New York City Department of Consumer Affairs Rules and Regulations as Amended. This sale is a Public Auction Sale conducted by Auctioneer. The New York City licensed auctioneers are: Kathleen Guzman, No. 0762165-Day, and Samuel W. Foose, No. 0952360-Day, No. 0952361-Night, who will conduct the Sale on behalf of Heritage Auctions, Inc. ("Auctioneer"). All lots are subject to: the consignor's rights to bid thereon in accord with these Terms and Conditions of Sale, consignor's option to receive advances on their consignments, and Auctioneer, in its sole discretion, may offer limited extended financing to registered bidders, in accord with Auctioneer's internal credit standards. A registered bidder may inquire whether a lot is subject to an advance or a reserve. Auctioneer has made advances to various consignors in this sale.

AUCTIONEER AND AUCTION:

1. This Auction is presented by Heritage Numismatic Auctions, Inc.; or its subsidiary Currency Auctions of America, Inc.; or their affiliate, Heritage Auctions, Inc. d/b/a Heritage Auction Galleries, Heritage Art Auctions, Heritage Fine & Decorative Arts Auctions, Heritage Comics Auctions, Heritage-Slater Americana, Heritage Vintage Movie Posters, or Heritage Sports Collectibles Auctions, as identified with the applicable licensing information on the title page of the catalog or on the Internet site (the "Auctioneer"). The Auction is conducted under these Terms and Conditions of Auction and applicable state and local law.

BUYER'S PREMIUM:

2. On bids placed through Heritage, a Buyer's Premium of fifteen percent (15%) for Heritage Numismatic Auctions Inc, Heritage-CAA, and Heritage Movie Posters or nineteen and one-half percent (19.5%) for Heritage Sports Collectibles, Heritage Comics Auctions, Heritage Music & Entertainment Memorabilia, Heritage Art Auctions and Heritage Americana of the hammer price will be added to the successful bid. If the bid is placed through eBay Live a Buyer's Premium equal to the normal Buyer's Premium plus an additional five percent (5%) of the hammer price will be added to the successful bid up to a maximum Buyer's Premium of Twenty Two and one-half percent (22.5%). There is a minimum Buyer's Premium of $9.00 per lot.

AUCTION VENUES:

3. Exclusively Internet, Continuous Internet, Internet Currency, Amazing Comics Auctions, Amazing Sports Auctions, and Online Session are Auctions conducted on the Internet. Signature Auctions accept bids on the Internet first, followed by a floor bidding session; bids may be placed prior to the floor bidding session by Internet, telephone, fax, or mail.

BIDDERS:

4. Any person participating or registering for the Auction agrees to be bound by and accepts these Terms and Conditions of Auction ("Bidder(s)").

5. All Bidders must meet Auctioneer's qualifications to bid. Any Bidder who is not a customer in good standing of the Auctioneer may be disqualified at Auctioneer's sole option and will not be awarded lots. Such a determination may be made by Auctioneer in its sole and unlimited discretion, at any time prior to, during, or even after the close of the Auction.

6. If an entity places a bid, then the person executing the bid on behalf of the entity agrees to personally guarantee payment for any successful bid.

7. Auctioneer reserves the right to exclude any person it deems in its sole opinion is disruptive to the Auction or is otherwise commercially unsuitable.

8. CREDIT REFERENCES: Bidders who do not have established credit with the Auctioneer must either furnish satisfactory credit information (including two collectibles-related business references) well in advance of the Auction or supply valid credit card information. Bids placed through our Interactive Internet program will only be accepted from pre-registered Bidders; Bidders who are not members of HeritageAuctions.com or affiliates should pre-register at least two business days before the first session to allow adequate time to contact references.

BIDDING OPTIONS:

9. Bids may be placed for a Signature Auction as set forth in the printed catalog section entitled "Choose your bidding method." For Exclusively Internet, Continuous Internet, Internet Currency, Amazing Comics Auctions, Amazing Sports Auctions, and Online Session auctions, see the alternatives shown on each website. Review at HeritageAuctions.com/common/howtobid.php.

10. Presentment of Bids: Non-Internet bids (including but not limited to podium, fax, phone and mail bids) are treated similar to floor bids in that they must be on-increment or at a half increment (called a cut bid). Any podium, fax, phone, or mail bids that do not conform to a full or half increment will be rounded up or down to the nearest full or half increment and will be considered your high bid.

11. Auctioneer's Execution of Certain Bids. Auctioneer cannot be responsible for your errors in bidding, so carefully check that each bid is entered correctly. When identical mail or FAX bids are submitted, preference is given to the first received. To ensure the greatest accuracy, your written bids should be entered on the standard printed bid sheet and be received at Auctioneer's place of business at least two business days before the Auction start. Auctioneer is not responsible for executing mail bids or FAX bids received on or after the day the first lot is sold, nor Internet bids submitted after the published closing time; nor is Auctioneer responsible for proper execution of bids submitted by telephone, mail, FAX, e-mail, Internet, or in person once the Auction begins. Internet bids may not be withdrawn until your written request is received and acknowledged by Auctioneer (FAX: 214-443-8425); such requests must state the reason, and may constitute grounds for withdrawal of bidding privileges. Lots won by mail Bidders will not be delivered at the Auction unless prearranged in advance. The decision of the Auctioneer and declaration of the winning Bidder is final.

12. Caveat as to Bids. Bid increments (over the current bid level) determine the lowest amount you may bid on a particular lot. Bids greater than one increment over the current bid can be any whole dollar amount. It is possible under several circumstances for winning bids to be between increments, sometimes only $1 above the previous increment. Please see: "How can I lose by less than an increment?" on our website.

13. Bidding Increments: The following chart governs current bidding increments.

Current Bid	Bid Increment	Current Bid	Bid Increment
< $10	$1	$3,000 - $4,999	$250
$10 - $29	$2	$5,000 - $9,999	$500
$30 - $59	$3	$10,000 - $19,999	$1,000
$60 - $99	$5	$20,000 - $29,999	$2,000
$100 - $199	$10	$30,000 - $49,999	$2,500
$200 - $299	$20	$50,000 - $99,999	$5,000
$300 - $499	$25	$100,000 - $249,999	$10,000
$500 - $999	$50	$250,000 - $499,999	$25,000
$1,000 - $1,999	$100	$500,000 - $1,499,999	$50,000
$2,000 - $2,999	$200	> $1,500,000	$100,000

CONDUCTING THE AUCTION:

14. Notice of the consignor's liberty to place reserve bids on his lots in the Auction is hereby made in accordance with Article 2 of the Texas Uniform Commercial Code. A reserve is an amount below which the lot will not sell. THE CONSIGNOR OF PROPERTY MAY PLACE WRITTEN RESERVE BIDS ON HIS LOTS IN ADVANCE OF THE AUCTION; ON SUCH LOTS, IF THE HAMMER PRICE DOES NOT MEET THE RESERVE, THE CONSIGNOR MAY PAY A REDUCED COMMISSION ON THOSE LOTS. Reserves

are generally posted online about 3 days prior to the Auction closing on Internet-Only Auctions, and 7 days prior to the Auction on Signature Auctions. Any successful bid placed by a consignor on his consigned lot on the Auction floor or by telephone during the live session, or after the reserves for an Auction have been posted, will be considered an unqualified bid, and in such instances the consignor agrees to pay full Buyer's Premium and Seller's Commissions on any lot so repurchased.

15. The highest qualified Bidder shall be the buyer. In the event of any dispute between floor Bidders at a Signature Auction, Auctioneer may at his sole discretion reoffer the lot. Auctioneer's decision shall be final and binding upon all Bidders.

16. Auctioneer reserves the right to refuse to honor any bid or to limit the amount of any bid which, in his sole discretion, is not submitted in "Good Faith," or is not supported by satisfactory credit, numismatic references, or otherwise. A bid is considered not made in "Good Faith" when an insolvent or irresponsible person, or a person under the age of eighteen makes it. Regardless of the disclosure of his identity, any bid by a consignor or his agent on a lot consigned by him is deemed to be made in "Good Faith." NOMINAL BIDS - The Auctioneer may at its sole discretion reject nominal bids, small opening bids or very nominal advances. If a lot fails to open for 40% to 60% of the low estimate, the Auctioneer may pass the item from the block to be re-offered at a subsequent auction, or may place a protective bid on behalf of the consignor.

17. All items are to be purchased per lot as numerically indicated and no lots will be broken. Auctioneer reserves the right to withdraw, prior to the close, any lots from the Auction.

18. Bids will be accepted in whole dollar amounts only. No "buy" or "unlimited" bids will be accepted. Bidders will be awarded lots at approximately the increment of the next highest bid. No additional commission is charged for executing bids. Off-increment bids may be accepted by the Auctioneer at Signature Auctions.

19. Auctioneer reserves the right to rescind the sale in the event of nonpayment, breach of a warranty, disputed ownership, auctioneer's clerical error or omission in exercising bids and reserves, or otherwise.

20. Outage Policy: Auctioneer occasionally experiences Internet and/or Server outages during which Bidders cannot participate or place bids. If such outage occurs, we may at our discretion extend bidding for the auction up to 24 hours. At our discretion, Auctioneer may consider two outages that occur very closely to one another to be one outage when extending such Auction. This policy applies only to widespread outages and not to isolated problems that occur in various parts of the country from time to time.

21. Scheduled Downtime: Auctioneer periodically schedules system downtime for maintenance and other purposes; this scheduled downtime is not covered by the Outage Policy.

22. The Auctioneer or its affiliates may consign items to be sold in the Auction, and may bid on those lots cr any other lots. Auctioneer or affiliates expressly reserve the right to modify any such reserve bids on these items or any others at any time prior to the live auction or the online closing based upon data made known to the Auctioneer or its affiliates. The Auctioneer may extend advances, guarantees, or loans to certain consignors, and may extend financing or other credits at varying rates to certain Bidders in the auction.

23. The Auctioneer has the right to sell certain items after the close of the sale. Items sold by Auctioneer post sale shall be considered sold during the auction and all these Terms and Conditions shall apply to such sales including but not limited to the payment of the buyer's fee, return rights and disclaimers.

PAYMENT:

24. All sales are strictly for cash in United States dollars. Cash includes: U.S. currency, bank wire, cashier checks, travelers checks, and bank money orders, all subject to reporting requirements. Credit Card (Visa or Master Card only) and PayPal payments may be accepted up to $10,000 from non-dealers at the sole discretion of the auctioneer, subject to the following limitations: a) sales are only to the cardholder, b) purchases are shipped to the cardholder's registered and verified address, c) Auctioneer may pre-approve the cardholder's credit line, d) a credit card transaction may not be used in conjunction with any other financing or extended terms offered by the Auctioneer, and must transact immediately upon invoice presentation, e) rights of return are governed by these Terms and Conditions, which supersede those conditions promulgated by the card issuer, f) floor Bidders must present their card. Personal or corporate checks may be subject to clearing before delivery of the purchases.

25. Payment is due upon closing of the Auction session, or upon presentment of an invoice. Auctioneer reserves the right to void an invoice if payment in full of the invoice is not received within 7 days after the close of the Auction.

26. Lots delivered in the States of Texas, California, or other states where the Auction may be held, are subject to all applicable state and local taxes, unless appropriate permits are on file with us. Bidder agrees to pay Auctioneer the actual amount of tax due in the event that sales tax is not properly collected due to: 1) an expired, inaccurate, inappropriate tax certificate or declaration, 2) an incorrect interpretation of the applicable statute, 3) or any other reason.. Lots from different Auctions may not be aggregated for sales tax purposes.

27. In the event that a Bidder's payment is dishonored upon presentment(s), Bidder shall pay the maximum statutory processing fee set by applicable state law.

28. If the Auction invoice(s) submitted by Auctioneer is not paid in full when due, the unpaid balance will bear interest at the highest rate permitted by law from the date of invoice until paid. If the Auctioneer refers the invoice(s) to an attorney for collection, the buyer agrees to pay attorney's fees, court costs, and other collection costs incurred by Auctioneer. If Auctioneer assigns collection to its in-house legal staff, such attorney's time expended on the matter shall be compensated at a rate comparable to the hourly rate of independent attorneys.

29. In the event a successful Bidder fails to pay all amounts due, Auctioneer reserves the right to resell the merchandise, and such Bidder agrees to pay for the reasonable costs of resale, including a 10% seller's commission, and also to pay any difference between the resale price and the price of the previously successful bid.

30. Auctioneer reserves the right to require payment in full in good funds before delivery of the merchandise to the buyer.

31. Auctioneer shall have a lien against the merchandise purchased by the buyer to secure payment of the Auction invoice. Auctioneer is further granted a lien and the right to retain possession of any other property of the buyer then held by the Auctioneer or its affiliates to secure payment of any Auction invoice or any other amounts due the Auctioneer from the buyer. With respect to these lien rights, Auctioneer shall have all the rights of a secured creditor under Article 9 of the Texas Uniform Commercial Code. In addition, with respect to payment of the Auction invoice(s), the buyer waives any and all rights of offset he might otherwise have against the Auctioneer and the consignor of the merchandise included on the invoice.

32. If a Bidder owes Auctioneer or its affiliates on any account, Auctioneer and its affiliates shall have the right to offset such unpaid account by any credit balance due Bidder, and it may secure by possessory lien any unpaid amount by any of the Bidder's property in their possession.

33. Title shall not pass to the successful Bidder until all invoices are paid in full. It is the responsibility of the buyer to provide adequate insurance coverage for the items once they have been delivered.

RETURN POLICIES:

34. A FINE ARTS, DECORATIVE ARTS OR MEMORABILIA lot (Autographs, Sports Collectibles, or Music, Entertainment, Political, Americana and/or Pop Culture memorabilia): The Auction is not on approval. When the lot is accompanied by a Certificate of Authenticity (or its equivalent) from an independent third party authentication provider, buyer has no right of return. Uncertified lots or under extremely limited circumstances not including authenticity (e.g. gross cataloging error), a purchaser who did not bid from the floor may request Auctioneer to evaluate voiding a sale; such request must be made in

writing detailing the alleged gross error, and submission of the lot to Auctioneer must be pre-approved by Auctioneer. A bidder must notify the appropriate department head (check the inside front cover of the catalog or our website for a listing of department heads) in writing of the purchaser's request and such notice must be mailed within three (3) days of the mail bidder's receipt of the lot. Any lot that is to be evaluated for return must be received in our offices within 30 days after Auction. AFTER THAT 30 DAY PERIOD, NO LOT MAY BE RETURNED FOR ANY REASONS. Lots returned must be in the same condition as when sold and must include the Certificate of Authenticity, if any. No lots purchased by floor bidders may be returned (including those bidders acting as agents for others). Late remittance for purchases may be considered just cause to revoke all return privileges.

35. COINS, CURRENCY, COMICS AND SPORTSCARDS Signature Auctions: The Auction is not on approval. No certified material may be returned because of possible differences of opinion with respect to the grade offered by any third-party organization, dealer, or service. No guarantee of grade is offered for uncertified Property sold and subsequently submitted to a third-party grading service. There are absolutely no exceptions to this policy. Under extremely limited circumstances, (e.g. gross cataloging error) a purchaser, who did not bid from the floor, may request Auctioneer to evaluate voiding a sale; such request must be made in writing detailing the alleged gross error, and submission of the lot to the Auctioneer must be pre-approved by the Auctioneer; bidder must notify Ron Brackemyre, (ext. 312) in writing of the such request and such notice must be mailed within three (3) days of the mail bidder's receipt of the lot. Any lot that is to be evaluated must be in our offices within 30 days after Auction. Grading or method of manufacture do not qualify for this evaluation process nor do such complaints constitute a basis to challenge the authenticity of a lot. AFTER THAT 30-DAY PERIOD, NO LOTS MAY BE RETURNED FOR REASONS OTHER THAN AUTHENTICITY. Lots returned must be housed intact in the original holder. No lots purchased by floor Bidders may be returned (including those Bidders acting as agents for others). Late remittance for purchases may be considered just cause to revoke all return privileges.

36. Exclusively Internet, Internet Currency, Amazing Comics Auctions, Amazing Sports Auctions, and Online Session auctions: THREE (3) DAY RETURN POLICY. All lots (Exception: Third party graded notes are not returnable for any reason whatsoever) paid for within seven days of the Auction closing are sold with a three (3) day return privilege. You may return lots under the following conditions: Within three days of receipt of the lot, you must first notify Auctioneer by contacting Customer Service by phone (1-800-872-6467) or e-mail (Bid@HeritageAuctions.com), and immediately mail the lot(s) fully insured to the attention of Returns, Heritage, 3500 Maple Avenue, 17th Floor, Dallas TX 75219-3941. Lots must be housed intact in their original holder and condition. You are responsible for the insured, safe delivery of any lots. A non-negotiable return fee of 5% of the purchase price ($10 per lot minimum) will be deducted from the refund for each returned lot or billed directly. Postage and handling fees are not refunded. After the three-day period (from receipt), no items may be returned for any reason. Late remittance for purchases revokes all Return-Restock privileges.

37. All Bidders who have inspected the lots prior to the auction will not be granted any return privileges, except for reasons of authenticity.

DELIVERY; SHIPPING AND HANDLING CHARGES:

38. Postage, handling and insurance charges will be added to invoices. Please either refer to Auctioneer's website HeritageAuctions.com/common/shipping.php for the latest charges or call Auctioneer.

39. Auctioneer is unable to combine purchases from other auctions or Heritage Rare Coin Galleries into one package for shipping purposes. Successful overseas Bidders shall provide written shipping instructions, including specified customs declarations, to the Auctioneer for any lots to be delivered outside of the United States. NOTE: Declaration value shall be the item(s) hammer price together with its buyer's premium.

40. All shipping charges will be borne by the successful Bidder. Due to the nature of some items sold, it shall be the responsibility for the successful bidder to arrange pick-up and shipping through third parties, as to such items Auctioneer shall have no liability. Any risk of loss during shipment will be borne by the buyer following Auctioneer's delivery to the designated common carrier, regardless of domestic or foreign shipment. Any request for shipping verification for undelivered packages must be made within 30 days of shipment by Auctioneer.

41. In the event an item is damaged either through handling or in transit, Auctioneer's maximum liability shall be the amount of the successful bid including the Buyer's Premium. On the fall of Auctioneer's hammer, Buyers of Fine Arts and Decorative Arts lots assumes full risk and responsibility for lot, including shipment by common carrier, and must provide their own insurance coverage for shipments.

CATALOGING, WARRANTIES AND DISCLAIMERS:

42. NO WARRANTY, WHETHER EXPRESSED OR IMPLIED, IS MADE WITH RESPECT TO ANY DESCRIPTION CONTAINED IN THIS AUCTION OR ANY SECOND OPINE. Any description of the items or second opine contained in this auction is for the sole purpose of identifying the items for those Bidders who do not have the opportunity to view the lots prior to bidding, and no description of items has been made part of the basis of the bargain or has created any express warranty that the goods would conform to any description made by Auctioneer.

43. Auctioneer is selling only such right or title to the items being sold as Auctioneer may have by virtue of consignment agreements on the date of auction and disclaims any warranty of title to the Property.

44. Translations of foreign language documents are provided as a convenience to interested parties. Heritage makes no representation as to the accuracy of those translations and will not be held responsible for errors in bidding arising from inaccuracies in translation.

45. In the event of an attribution error, Auctioneer may at its sole discretion, correct the error on the Internet, or, if discovered at a later date, to refund the buyer's money without further obligation. Under no circumstances shall the obligation of the Auctioneer to any Bidder be in excess of the purchase price for any lot in dispute.

46. Auctioneer disclaims any warranty of merchantability or fitness for any particular purposes.

47. Auctioneer disclaims all liability for damages, consequential or otherwise, arising out of or in connection with the sale of any property by Auctioneer to Bidder. No third party may rely on any benefit of these Terms and Conditions and any rights, if any, established hereunder are personal to the Bidder and may not be assigned. Any statement made by the Auctioneer is an opinion and does not constitute a warranty or representation. No employee of Auctioneer may alter these Terms and Conditions, and, unless signed by a principal of Auctioneer, any such alteration is null and void.

48F. FINE AND DECORATIVE ARTS – Auctioneer warrants bold-faced items in the descriptions, which are otherwise provided for identification purposes only. Bidders who intend to challenge the bold-faced items in the descriptions of a lot must notify Auctioneer in writing within thirty (30) days of the Auction's conclusion. Auctioneer's maximum liability shall not exceed the high bid on that lot, which bid shall be deemed for all purposes the value of the lot. In the event Auctioneer cannot deliver the lot or subsequently it is established that the lot lacks title, provenance, authenticity, or other transfer or condition issue is claimed, Auctioneer's liability shall be limited to recission of sale and refund of purchase price. After one year has elapsed, Auctioneer's maximum liability shall be limited to any commissions and fees Auctioneer earned on that lot. Nothwitstanding any other provision, while title to an item is warranted, authenticity or provenance is a matter of opinion and is not warranted or part of Auctioneer's representations.

49. All non-certified coins, currency, and comics are guaranteed genuine, but are not guaranteed as to grade, since grading is a matter of opinion, an art and not a science, and therefore the opinion rendered by the Auctioneer or any third party grading service may not agree with the opinion of others (including trained experts), and the same expert may not grade the same item with the same grade at two different times. Auctioneer has graded the non-certified numismatic items, in the Auctioneer's opinion, to their current interpretation of the American Numismatic Association's standards as of the date the catalog was prepared. There is no guarantee or warranty implied or expressed that the grading standards utilized by the Auctioneer will meet the standards of ANACS, NGC, PCGS, ICG, CGC, CGA or any other grading service at any time in the future.

50. Since we cannot examine encapsulated notes or comics, they are sold "as is" without our grading opinion, and may not be returned for any reason. Auctioneer shall not be liable for any patent or latent defect or controversy pertaining to or arising from any encapsulated collectible. In any such instance, purchaser's remedy, if any, shall be solely against the service certifying the collectible.

51. Due to changing grading standards over time, differing interpretations, and to possible mishandling of items by subsequent owners, Auctioneer reserves the right to grade items differently than shown on certificates from any grading service that accompany the items. Auctioneer also reserves the right to grade items differently than the grades shown in the catalog should such items be reconsigned to any future auction.

52. Although consensus grading is employed by most grading services, it should be noted as aforesaid that grading is not an exact science. In fact, it is entirely possible that if a lot is broken out of a plastic holder and resubmitted to another grading service or even to the same service, the lot could come back with a different grade assigned.

53. Certification does not guarantee protection against the normal risks associated with potentially volatile markets. The degree of liquidity for certified coins and collectibles will vary according to general market conditions and the particular lot involved. For some lots there may be no active market at all at certain points in time.

RELEASE:

54. In consideration of participation in the auction and the placing of a bid, a Bidder expressly releases Auctioneer, its officers, directors and employees, its affiliates, and its outside experts that provide second opines from any and all claims, cause of action, chose of action, whether at law or equity or any arbitration or mediation rights existing under the rules of any professional society or affiliation based upon the assigned grade or a derivative theory, breach of warranty express or implied, representation or other matter set forth within these Terms and Conditions of Auction or otherwise, except as specifically declared herein; e.g., authenticity, typographical error, etc., and as to those matters, the rights and privileges conferred therein are strictly construed and is the exclusive remedy. Purchaser, by non-compliance to its express terms of a granted remedy, shall waive any claim against Auctioneer.

DISPUTE RESOLUTION AND ARBITRATION PROVISION:

55. By placing a bid or otherwise participating in the auction, such person or entity accepts these Terms and Conditions of Auction, and specifically agrees to the alternative dispute resolution provided herein. Arbitration replaces the right to go to court, including the right to a jury trial.

56. Auctioneer in no event shall be responsible for consequential damages, incidental damages, compensatory damages, or other damages arising from the auction of any lot. Auctioneer's maximum liability shall not exceed the high bid on that lot, which bid shall be deemed for all purposes the value of the lot. In the event that Auctioneer cannot deliver the lot or subsequently it is established that the lot lacks title, provenance, authenticity, or other transfer or condition issue is claimed, Auctioneer's liability shall be limited to recission of sale and refund of purchase price. After one year has elapsed, Auctioneer's maximum liability shall be limited to any commissions and fees Auctioneer earned on that lot.

57. Any claim as to provenance or authenticity must be first transmitted to Auctioneer by credible and definitive evidence and there is no assurance after such presentment that Auctioneer will validate the claim. Authentication is not an exact science and contrary opinions may not be recognized by Auctioneer. Even if Auctioneer agrees with the contrary opinion of such authentication, our liability for reimbursement for such service shall not exceed $500.

58. Provenance and authenticity are not guaranteed by the Auctioneer, but rather are guaranteed by the consignor. Any action or claim shall include the consignor with Auctioneer acting as interpleador or nominal party. While every effort is made to determine provenance and authenticity, it is up to the Bidder to arrive at that conclusion prior to bidding.

59. If any dispute arises regarding payment, authenticity, grading, description, provenance, or any other matter pertaining to the Auction, the Bidder or a participant in the Auction and/or the Auctioneer agree that the dispute shall be submitted, if otherwise mutually unresolved, to binding arbitration in accordance with the commercial rules of the American Arbitration Association (A.A.A.). A.A.A. arbitration shall be conducted under the provisions of the Federal Arbitration Act with locale in Dallas, Texas. Any claim made by a Bidder has to be presented within one (1) year or it is barred. The prevailing party may be awarded his reasonable attorney's fees and costs. An award granted in arbitration is enforceable in any court of competent jurisdiction. No claims of any kind (except for reasons of authenticity) can be considered after the settlements have been made with the consignors. Any dispute after the settlement date is strictly between the Bidder and consignor without involvement or responsibility of the Auctioneer. NOTE: Purchasers of rare coins or currency through Heritage have available the option of arbitration by the Professional Numismatists Guild (PNG); if an election is not made within ten (10) days of an unresolved dispute, Auctioneer may elect either PNG or A.A.A. Arbitration.

60. In consideration of his participation in or application for the auction, a person or entity (whether the successful Bidder, a Bidder, a purchaser and/or other Auction participant or registrant) agrees that all disputes in any way relating to, arising under, connected with, or incidental to these Terms and Conditions and purchases or default in payment thereof shall be arbitrated pursuant to the arbitration provision. In the event that any matter including actions to compel arbitration, construe the agreement, actions in aid or arbitration or otherwise needs to be litigated, such litigation shall be exclusively in the Courts of the State of Texas, in Dallas County, Texas, and if necessary the corresponding appellate courts. The successful Bidder, purchaser, or Auction participant also expressly submits himself to the personal jurisdiction of the State of Texas.

MISCELLANEOUS:

61. Agreements between Bidders and consignors to effectuate a non-sale of an item at Auction, inhibit bidding on a consigned item to enter into a private sale agreement for said item, or to utilize the Auctioneer's Auction to obtain sales for non-selling consigned items subsequent to the auction, are strictly prohibited. If a subsequent sale of a previously consigned item occurs in violation of this provision, Auctioneer reserves the right to charge Bidder the applicable Buyer's Premium and consignor a Seller's Commission as determined for each auction venue and by the terms of the seller's agreement.

62. Acceptance of these terms and conditions qualifies Bidder as a Heritage customer who has consented to be contacted by Heritage in the future. In conformity with "do-not-call" regulations promulgated by the Federal or State regulatory agencies, participation by the Bidder is affirmative consent to being contacted at the phone number shown in his application and this consent shall remain in effect until it is revoked in writing. Heritage may from time to time contact Bidder concerning sale, purchase and auction opportunities available through Heritage and its affiliates and subsidiaries.

63. Storage of purchased coins and currency: Purchasers are advised that certain types of plastic may react with a coin's metal or transfer plasticizer to notes and may cause damage. Caution should be used to avoid storage in materials that are not inert.

STATE NOTICES:

64. Notice as to an Auction Sale in California. Auctioneer has in compliance with Title 2.95 of the California Civil Code as amended October 11, 1993 Sec. 1812.600, posted with the California Secretary of State its bonds for it and its employees and the auction is being conducted in compliance with Sec. 2338 of the Commercial Code and Sec. 535 of the Penal Code.

Rev. 7_20_06

Mail Bidding at Auction

Mail bidding at auction is fun and easy and only requires a few simple steps.

1. Look through the catalog, and determine the lots of interest.

2. Research their market value by checking price lists and other price guidelines.

3. Fill out your bid sheet, entering your maximum bid on each lot.

4. Verify your bids!

5. Mail Early. Preference is given to the first bids received in case of a tie. When bidding by mail, you frequently purchase items at less than your maximum bid.

Bidding is opened at the published increment above the second highest mail or Internet bid; we act on your behalf as the highest mail bidder. If bidding proceeds, we act as your agent, bidding in increments over the previous bid. This process is continued until you are awarded the lot or you are outbid.

An example of this procedure: You submit a bid of $100, and the second highest mail bid is at $50. Bidding starts at $51 on your behalf. If no other bids are placed, you purchase the lot for $51. If other bids are placed, we bid for you in the posted increments until we reach your maximum bid of $100. If bidding passes your maximum: if you are bidding through the Internet, we will contact you by e-mail; if you bid by mail, we take no other action. Bidding continues until the final bidder wins.

Telephone Bidding

To participate by telephone, please make arrangements at least one week before the sale date with Customer Service, 1-800-872-6467, Ext. 150.

We strongly recommend that you place preliminary bids by mail, fax, or Internet, even if you intend to participate by telephone. On many occasions this dual approach has helped reduce disappointments due to telephone problems, unexpected travel, late night sessions and time zone differences, etc. We will make sure that you do not bid against yourself.

Mail Bidding Instructions

1. **Name, Address, City, State, Zip**
   Your address is needed to mail your purchases. We need your telephone number to communicate any problems or changes that may affect your bids.

2. **References**
   If you have not established credit with us from previous auctions, you must send a 25% deposit, or list dealers with whom you have credit established.

3. **Lot Numbers and Bids**
   List all lots you desire to purchase. On the reverse are additional columns; you may also use another sheet. Under "Amount" enter the maximum you would pay for that lot (whole dollar amounts only). We will purchase the lot(s) for you as much below your bids as possible.

4. **Total Bid Sheet**
   Add up all bids and list that total in the appropriate box.

5. **Sign Your Bid Sheet**
   By signing the bid sheet, you have agreed to abide by the Terms of Auction listed in the auction catalog.

6. **Fax Your Bid Sheet**
   When time is short submit a Mail Bid Sheet on our exclusive Fax Hotline. There's no faster method to get your bids to us *instantly*. Simply use the **Heritage Fax Hotline number: 214-443-8425**.

   When you send us your original after faxing, mark it "Confirmation of Fax" (preferably in red!)

7. **Bidding Increments**
   To facilitate bidding, please consult the following chart. Bids will be accepted on the increments or on the half increments.

The official prices realized list that accompanies our auction catalogs is reserved for bidders and consignors only. We are happy to mail one to others upon receipt of $1.00. Written requests should be directed to Customer Service.

Interactive Internet™ Bidding

You can now bid with Heritage's exclusive *Interactive Internet*™ program, available only at our web site: HA.com. It's fun, and it's easy!

1. Register online at:
   HA.com

2. View the full-color photography of every single lot in the online catalog!

3. Construct your own personal catalog for preview.

4. View the current opening bids on lots you want; review the prices realized archive.

5. Bid and receive immediate notification if you are the top bidder; later, if someone else bids higher, you will be notified automatically by e-mail.

6. The *Interactive Internet*™ program opens the lot on the floor at one increment over the second highest bid. As the high bidder, your secret maximum bid will compete for you during the floor auction, and it is possible that you may be outbid on the floor after Internet bidding closes. Bid early, as the earliest bird wins in the event of a tie bid.

7. After the sale, you will be notified of your success. It's that easy!

Interactive Internet™ Bidding Instructions

1. **Log Onto Website**

   Log onto **HA.com** and chose the portal you're interested in (i.e., coins, comics, movie posters, fine arts, etc.).

2. **Search for Lots**

   Search or browse for the lot you are interested in. You can do this from the home page, from the Auctions home page, or from the home page for the particular auction in which you wish to participate.

3. **Select Lots**

   Click on the link or the photo icon for the lot you want to bid on.

4. **Enter Bid**

   At the top of the page, next to a small picture of the item, is a box outlining the current bid. Enter the amount of your secret maximum bid in the textbox next to "Secret Maximum Bid." The secret maximum bid is the maximum amount you are willing to pay for the item you are bidding on (for more information about bidding and bid increments, please see the section labeled "Bidding Increments" elsewhere in this catalog). Click on the button marked "Place Absentee Bid." A new area on the same page will open up for you to enter your username (or e-mail address) and password. Enter these, then click "Place Absentee Bid" again.

5. **Confirm Absentee Bid**

   You are taken to a page labeled, "Please Confirm Your Bid." This page shows you the name of the item you're bidding on, the current bid, and the maximum bid. When you are satisfied that all the information shown is correct, click on the button labeled, "Confirm Bid."

6. **Bidding Status Notification**

   One of two pages is now displayed.

   a. If your bid is the current high bid, you will be notified and given additional information as to what might happen to affect your high bidder status over the course of the remainder of the auction. You will also receive a Bid Confirmation notice via email.

   b. If your bid is not the current high bid, you will be notified of that fact and given the opportunity to increase your bid.